David & Charles Locomotive Studies

SULZER
DIESEL LOCOMOTIVES
OF
BRITISH RAIL

Brian Webb

DAVID & CHARLES
NEWTON ABBOT   LONDON   NORTH POMFRET (VT)

David & Charles Locomotive Studies

Published titles still in print

Diesel-hydraulic Locomotives of the Western Region, by Brian Reed

The Drummond Greyhounds of the LSWR, by D. L. Bradley

Stanier 4-6-0s of the LMS, by J. W. P. Rowledge and Brian Reed

Locomotive Monographs

All by O. S. Nock, BSc, CEng, FICE, FIMechE

The GWR Stars, Castles and Kings

Gresley Pacifics, Parts 1 and 2

The Southern King Arthur Family

Royal Scots and Patriots of the LMS

British Library Cataloguing in Publication Data

Webb, Brian
　Sulzer diesel locomotives of British Rail.—
　(David and Charles locomotive studies).
　1. Sulzer Brothers UK Ltd　2. British Rail
　3. Diesel locomotives—Great Britain—History
　I. Title
　385′.36′620941　　TJ619

　ISBN 0-7153-7514-8

Library of Congress Catalog Card Number 78-52162

© Brian Webb 1978

First published 1978
Second impression 1980

Printed in Great Britain
by Biddles Limited Guildford
for David & Charles (Publishers) Limited
Brunel House Newton Abbot Devon

Published in the United States of America
by David & Charles Inc
North Pomfret Vermont 05053 USA

CONTENTS

INTRODUCTION

In 1977 all British Railways diesel electric locomotives from 350 to 3250bhp are powered by either Sulzer or English Electric types of diesel engines. This is remarkable in view of the vast array of engine makes and types delivered to BR from 1957.

Sulzer has powered 1,398 of BR diesel locomotives, and English Electric 2,082. Of these, Sulzer has powered by far the greatest number of main line locomotives, the figures for locomotives from 1000bhp upwards being 1,398 for Sulzer and 819 for English Electric.

At the end of the day it is no coincidence that it is the low-/medium-speed diesel engine which has won the day. Experiences throughout many countries show that it is the diesel engine with the smallest number of cylinders of large bore, minimum of components and working parts, which gives maximum overall advantage. These engines can run for considerable periods and have long lives. Both Sulzer and English Electric engines fall into this category.

The marriage of relatively heavy engine/generator sets with unduly heavy mechanical structures initially brought trouble to BR, but well within the first decade of dieselisation on BR the wheel turned full circle and 2700/2750bhp diesel-electrics of 114 tons plus service weight were in large-scale production.

The resulting standardisation of the Sulzer and English Electric engines is therefore not surprising. In spite of the viscisitudes which beset the Sulzer twin-bank engine, it and its in-line compatriots are still working away on BR hauling the majority of its traffic, be it fast Inter-City passenger, slow mineral trains, or Freightliners. The Sulzer engine has earned its niche in railway history.

Covering satisfactorily the numerically large fleet of Sulzer-powered diesel locomotives on BR has provoked problems, not the least of which is the complex renumbering introduced from October 1968. The original locomotive numbers with the 'D' prefix are mostly used for ease of identity, sufficient tables being provided to give the current position.

For locomotive classification the author has adopted the new numerical system from the start, and while this may upset purists it is certainly easier to talk about a class 47 than a Brush type 4.

The numerically largest Sulzer types have received most coverage because of their relative importance. Definitive treatment is not intended; this must come with retrospective histories. An attempt has been made to give a general history of the locomotives involved rather than produce a treatise on diesel traction practice.

Although much has been said about personalities and names of those associated with the large involvement of BR with the Sulzer engine, the author has not entered into the argument here, as this is not the time to do so, although some may disagree. The research of contemporary rail traction brings with it many commercial considerations, so some information is not at this time available for publication.

The author wishes to record his grateful thanks to the following organisations for providing information, permitting research, and allowing certain illustrations to be used: Brush Electrical Machines Ltd, Sulzer Bros UK Ltd, GEC Traction Ltd, British Railways. The assistance of the following people is also thankfully recorded: Messrs Norman B. Gardener, M. Scott, G. S. Toms, F. H. Wood, D. R. Minkley, A. Tayler, D. C. Plyer and Alan Simpson.

Assistance with illustrations and photographs has come from Messrs Ian S. Carr, Peter W. Robinson, Derek Cross, John A. Howie, Fred Kerr, N. E. Preedy, British Railways, GEC Traction Ltd, Brush Electrical Machines Ltd, Sulzer Bros UK Ltd, A. C. Baker and J. Robin Lidster.

Members and officers of the Railway Correspondence & Travel Society, Stephenson Locomotive Society, and those kindred spirits of the Diesel & Electric Group, have given their time and supported the work.

Michael J. Oakley, with his speciality in locomotive performance, has been very generous and helpful in preparing the information on which chapter 8 is largely based, special thanks being due in this respect.

The manuscript was typed by Deborah L. Scheetz, who did an excellent job of translating many rough notes and amendments, plus eleventh-hour alterations, into a readable text.

Brian Webb
December 1977

CHAPTER 1

SULZER IN RAIL TRACTION

In 1911/2 the Thermolocomotive Co.—involving Sulzer Bros, Dr Rudolph Diesel, Adolf Klose, and the German locomotive builder Borsig—completed and placed on rails the first attempt at a main line locomotive of high power propelled by a form of compression-ignition 'diesel' engine. Although this in no way supports the much publicised idea that Dr Diesel invented the engine erroneously called after him today, Sulzer can claim through this early association that it was in at the start of this form of traction. The locomotive was a 95-ton 2-B-2 of 1000bhp fitted with a Sulzer-built vee-type engine, driving directly to the locomotive wheels. Initial starting was accomplished by compressed air until, at a suitable speed, the 'diesel' engine was brought in. The locomotive was a failure, although it did run in Switzerland and in Prussia.

One of the main figures at Sulzer Bros was Adolf Brunner. He was involved in the above project and, supported by Robert Sulzer, became chief engineer at Sulzer. Brunner was responsible for rail traction work and, although Sulzer itself never built a locomotive, the firm involved in locomotive design, and acted as main contractors in some instances. Brunner's work on the development of the Sulzer engine automatic regulation system, controlling economical performance and protection against overloading, should be noted.

In 1914 five Sulzer diesel engines of four-stroke, vee-type with pre-combustion chambers and air-injection were fitted in diesel electric railcars for the Val-de-Travers railway in Switzerland. These engines, of 200bhp and 440rpm, were converted to solid fuel injection in 1922, and are thought to be still at work today. From that date it is interesting to record Sulzer's preference for the diesel-electric locomotive rather than the diesel-hydraulic.

The engine range was applied and developed, but no more vee-type engines were built from 1927 until the mid-1950s. In the 1920s the LV engine range of 180–1200bhp, covering ten models with several cylinder sizes, was introduced. These open-type, pre-combustion chamber engines had individually-cast cylinders and fabricated steel underbeds of riveted construction which carried the engine and main generator. The change from air-blast to solid-fuel injection took place at the change from vee- to in-line engines at Sulzer's in 1927/8.

So far as the UK is concerned, it was Sir W. G. Armstrong, Whitworth & Co. (Engineers) Ltd of Scotswood, Newcastle upon Tyne (AW), which took up the Sulzer engine for rail traction. AW set up its diesel traction department in 1930/1, following a minor role with some 600 and 1200bhp locomotive and mobile power-house work for the Buenos Aires Great Southern Railway. By 1931 AW was building Sulzer rail-traction engines at Scotswood under licence, completing the first railcars, shunters and main line locomotives by 1933 for use in the UK and overseas. All these were diesel-electrics. A total of 29 Sulzer-engined diesel-electrics was built by AW between 1931 and 1937, of which 16 were employed in the UK. Their work included units up to 1700bhp, at the time the most powerful in the world.

The Sulzer LDA engine range emerged during the 1930s, but the twin-bank engine did not replace the 12LDA31 unit until 1937/8. Although never so standardised as the engines of the English Electric Co. Ltd, having several cylinder sizes, it was available in the 400–2200bhp range by 1937/8.

After the end of hostilities in 1945, the twin-bank 12LDA28 engine was rated at 2000bhp at 750rpm in 1954/5, then 2300bhp in 1955/6, 2500bhp with charge-air cooling, and finally 2750bhp at 800rpm. At its time it was the highest rated rail-traction diesel in the world.

The first main line diesel-electrics having Sulzer engines owned by a railway in the British Isles were two 80-ton Bo-Bo units of 915bhp, built at the Inchicore (Dublin) works of Coras Iompair Eireann (CIE) in 1951. Intended as mixed-traffic locomotives, these Metropolitan-Vickers equipped locomotives with their top speed of 50mph were used mostly on freight and parcels trains between Dublin and Cork. They did, in fact, introduce CIE to diesel traction, and in so doing took that railway from antiquated steam power to diesel without touching modern steam locomotion, apart from a handful of such locomotives. Their engines were the 6LDA28 model, running at 750rpm and later uprated to 960bhp.

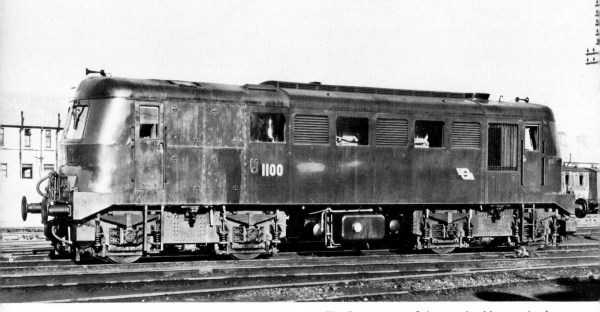

The first post-war Sulzer-engined locomotive for use in the British Isles was this 915bhp diesel-electric for the CIE in Eire. Two locomotives numbered 1100/1 were built at Inchicore works in 1951, with electrical equipment by Metropolitan Vickers Ltd. *(GEC Traction)*

CIE decided to order further 915bhp locomotives, and Vickers Ltd of Barrow-in-Furness built the Sulzer engines—their first. It was originally intended to have six twin-engined 1800bhp locomotives for Dublin–Cork expresses, but the idea was caught up in a policy change and put in limbo. It was not until 1956/7 that these 12 engines appeared on 12 A1A-A1A diesel-electrics built at the works of Birmingham Railway Carriage & Wagon Co. Ltd (BRCW) at Smethwick. The 6LDA28 engine was set at 960bhp continuous rating and 1000bhp at one-hour rating. These 75-ton locomotives had Metropolitan-Vickers electrical equipment and they had, interestingly, modified Pennsylvania-type bogies, a type also used by BRCW on exported Sulzer-powered locomotives.

The association of BRCW with the Sulzer engine stemmed from this initial order, but it was not until a working agreement took shape between BRCW, Sulzer Bros and Crompton, Parkinson Ltd (CP) that things really got under way. The result of this agreement was a standard A1A-A1A diesel-electric of 900/1000bhp, using the 6LDA28 engine and Crompton, Parkinson (CP) electrics. A total of 20 locomotives was built in 1954, 1955 and 1960 for Commonwealth Railways and Sierra Leone Development Corporation. One of the former did running trials on BR with standard gauge bogies during 1954, in the Birmingham area. Out of 260 diesel-electric locomotives built by BRCW, only 13 did not have Sulzer engines.

After the demise of BRCW, the 6LDA28

engine found further export application in a new consortium involving Sulzer Bros, Associated Electrical Industries (AEI) and Metropolitan Cammell Ltd. The inter-cooled engine was used in a standard 1200bhp Co-Co diesel-electric designed for African countries (the Zambezi class), then as a 1400bhp development. It was supplied to Malawi, Mozambique and Nigeria to a total of 53 units. Experience with the engine on BR played a big part in this work.

During the mid 1950s the new Sulzer vee-type engine LVA24 was developed and built for use by the SNCF in France from 1960/1. An 8-, 12- and 16-cylinder range of 1750-4000bhp was finally offered. This range subsequently became the AS range, and at this point development rests. Ten French-built 12LVA24 engines of 2500bhp were incorporated in Co-Co diesel-electrics supplied by Clayton Equipment Co. Ltd to Cuba in 1965/6. At the time of their appearance they were the most powerful UK-built exported diesel locomotives.

So far as can be seen, no tangible results have come from the agreement between English Electric and Sulzer for development and manufacture of the LVA engine range, EE going ahead with the development of its own engine designs to meet increasing power demands.

TABLE 1
COMPARATIVE DIMENSIONS AND MAIN DETAILS OF BR SULZER LOCOMOTIVES, 1958 TO DATE

Class	Builder	Axle layout	Bhp	Electrical equipment maker	Service weight range tons cwt	Overall length ft in	Overall width ft in	Overall height ft in	Driving wheel diameter ft in	Carrying wheel diameter ft in	Bogie wheelbase ft in	Bogie centres ft in	Total wheelbase ft in	Maximum speed mph	Maximum tractive effort lb	Continuous tractive effort lb/mph
24	Derby Crewe Darlington	Bo-Bo	1160	BTH	71 0 to 79 16	50 6	9 1	12 8	3 9	—	8 6	28 0	36 6	75	40,000	21,300/14·8
25	Derby Darlington Beyer Peacock	Bo-Bo	1250	BTH AEI	70 5 to 74 8	50 6	9 1	12 8	3 9	—	8 6	28 0	36 6	90	39,000 and 45,000	20,800/17·1
26	BRCW	Bo-Bo	1160	CP	73 6 to 77 17	50 9	8 10	12 8	3 7	—	10 0	29 0	39 0	75	42,000	30,000/ 11·25
27	BRCW	Bo-Bo	1250	GEC	71 4 to 76 1	50 9	8 10	12 8	3 7	—	10 0	29 0	39 0	90	40,000	25,000/14·0
33	BRCW	Bo-Bo	1550	CP	76 5 to 77 6	50 9	8 5½ and 8 10	12 8	3 7	—	10 0	29 0	39 0	85	45,000	26,000/17·5
44	Derby	1Co-Co1	2300	CP	138 2	67 11	8 10	12 10⅛	3 9	3 0	21 6	32 8	59 8	90	70,000 later 55,000	41,000/16·5 later 30,000/25·0
45	Crewe Derby	1Co-Co1	2500	CP	132 16 to 135 7	67 11	9 1 9/16	12 10	3 9	3 0	21 6	32 8	59 8	90	55,000	30,000/25·0
46	Derby	1Co-Co1	2500	Brush	138 4 to 138 6	67 11	9 1 9/16	12 10	3 9	3 0	21 6	32 8	59 8	90	55,000	31,600/23·3
47	Brush Traction Crewe	Co-Co	2750 later 2580	Brush	111 18 to 123 4	63 7	9 2	12 9⅜	3 9	—	14 6	37 0	51 6	95	55,000 and 62,000	30,000/27·0
48	Brush Traction	Co-Co	2650 later 2580	Brush	111 12	63 7	9 2	12 9⅜	3 9	—	14 6	37 0	51 6	95	62,000	30,000/26·2 later 30,000/27·0
Lion	BRCW	Co-Co	2750	AEI	114 0	63 6	8 10	12 9⅜	3 9	—	14 6	36 3	50 9	100	55,000	30,000/25·5
Kestrel	Brush Traction	Co-Co	3775	Brush	133 0	66 6	8 9¾	12 9¾	3 7	—	14 11 later 14 6	37 2	51 8	130	70,000	41,000/27·5

CHAPTER 2
THE SULZER DIESEL ENGINE ON BRITISH RAIL

Apart from a small number of imports from Winterthur and Mantes (France), the vast majority of the 1,400 Sulzer-powered diesel locomotives on BR since 1958 incorporate the Barrow-in-Furness built engines from Vickers Ltd, acting as sub-contractor to Sulzer Bros (London) Ltd. The agreement between Sulzer and Vickers was first put into practice in 1949/50, but large-scale production did not start until 1957, with the inception of the BR modernisation programme.

The selection of a Swiss diesel engine design for such a large number of BR locomotives provoked much conjecture, for suggestions that BR purchase USA-built diesel locomotives rather than British locomotives provided fierce political arguments, and were of course squashed at an early date. In the case of the Sulzer engine, the tooling-up of Vickers and its large involvement in the production of the engine in the UK was probably again politically dictated, while at the same time bringing work to the Barrow area.

At the time of the ordering of BR diesel locomotive power equipment in the first orders of 1955, the influence of J. F. Harrison, then chief mechanical engineer, on BR thinking must be noted, for at that time there was a decided preference for the Sulzer engine at Derby. This seemed strange in view of Derby works' previous involvement with the EE engine, although the influence of C. E. Fairburn (an ex-EE man) must also be taken into account. Perhaps J. F. Harrison, who was an ex-LNER man and pro-Gresley, brought a 'new broom' to Derby which swept away things LMSR and EE—for a time at least.

So far as BR is concerned, Vickers built three types of Sulzer diesels: the 6LDA28 model, of 1160/1250bhp; the 8LDA28, of 1550bhp; and the 12LDA28 twin-bank engine of 2300/2750bhp. The engine identification code terminology used by Sulzer is explained thus: taking 12LDA28C for an example, 12 = number of cylinders, L = traction (locomotive), D = direct injection, A = blown or turbo-charged, 28 = cylinder bore in centimetres, C = model with a degree of inter-cooling. From a slow start, engine production at Barrow built up to 12 to 15 engines per month.

To comply with BR requirements, many modifications and variations in ancillary equipment were included in the British-built engines. CAV or Bryce single-unit injection pumps and fuel injectors were used. These, however, had Sulzer-design plungers which varied the injection timing automatically according to loading. Turbo-blowers of Sulzer type, but British-built, were fitted; these have Vokes circular oil-wetted air-filters instead of the centrifugal model. Engine oil cooling involves a heat exchanger on the engine underbed, which itself forms part of the crankcase structure. Pipework has been virtually removed from the exterior of the engine. Internal development of the engine produced main bearing changes to those of precision-type with thin

Cross-section through the Sulzer LDA28 in-line engine which is used in the power range 1160–1550 bhp in BR locomotives.   *(Sulzer Bros UK Ltd)*

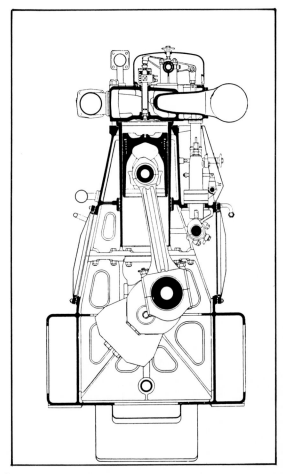

steel shells and copper-lead linings. Bearing housings were unchanged. The big-ends had similar bearings.

Building practice at Barrow—a works with diesel engine experience going back to before the 1914-18 war—involved a large shop equipped with jigs for welding-up fabrications, and well equipped with machine tools. Stress-relieved components, together with building-up from the crankcase/underbed on its four resilient pads, were used to give good alignment and assembly procedures for cylinder bores and crankshaft bearings. Cleanliness during erection and test-bed stage, and flushing through with hot oil for eight hours preceded actual testing.

Dealing with the engines in order of output, the first is the 6LDA28 six-cylinder in-line vertical engine with 11·2in × 14·4in cylinders (bore × stroke). This pressure-charged engine was first applied on BR at 1160bhp running at 750rpm in its 'A' version. The bmep at this output is rated at 150lb/sq in, although a one-hour test at 1276bhp was included in the acceptance trials. At full load the fuel consumption is 0·358lb/bhp per hour; mean piston speed is 1770ft/min. This engine is used in BR classes 24 and 26.

In the 'B' version, output is 1250bhp at 750rpm by provision of an air-to-water, free-flow inter-cooler between pressure charger and the inlet manifold. The inter-cooler is included in the normal cooling water circuit to avoid separate pumps and radiator cooling circuit elements. Bmep at 1250bhp is raised to 165lb/sq in; the one-hour rating is 1375bhp. At full load, fuel consumption is 0·37lb/bhp per hour, at half load 0·36lb/bhp per hour. The difference in engine dry weights is 9·6 tons and 9·7 tons; cylinder hp is 190 and 210 per cylinder respectively.

The crankcase is fabricated by welding from seven cast-steel cross-pieces, each with a bearing housing, and box-section steel side plates. The latter are extended to form a base for generator mounting. The cylinder block is mounted on top of the steel frames. The sump is of steel and welded to the bottom of the crankcase. Main oil pipes are integrally welded into the structure. Bearing caps are anchored in a recess in the steel frame and have retaining wedges locked in by keep plates. Pre-finished, tri-metal bearings requiring no hand fitting or adjustment on assembly are fitted.

The cylinder block is of seven cast-steel frames surmounted by a forged-steel top deck-plate and water jacket. The block incorporates housings

for the camshaft bearings. Flanged wet-liners are clamped between the top face of the block and the cylinder heads with spigot location in each face. Water sealing rings are in grooves at the bottom end of the liner and allow for longitudinal expansion. The liners themselves are honed/ground in the bore and externally tapered to save weight. Each cylinder has an individual cast-iron head with one inlet, and one outlet valve; the valves are interchangeable. Each valve push-rod is enclosed in a rubber sleeve with sufficient size to allow rocker oil return and breathing. The push-rods are pin-jointed to the rockers with a tappet adjusting screw in the fork end. The fuel injector is centrally placed on each cylinder.

The inlet manifold is on the camshaft side and the inlet port is designed to give good 'swirl' characteristics and high efficiency with the use of the single valve. Valve heads are sited in depressions in the face of the head with main combustion space provided for in the recessed piston head. The pistons are of aluminium-alloy, two-piece forgings, machined all over. The piston ring carrier, with three compression and one scraper ring, is a shrunk-on sleeve allowing provision of pressure-fed cooling oil grooves behind the rings, the feed coming from drillings in the gudgeon-pin boss. Fully floating gudgeon pins retained by circlips are used.

A seven-bearing alloy steel crankshaft with oval webs and bolted-on balance weights is fitted. This is bored through at the journals and crank pins, eliminating the need for diagonal drilling of webs for oil distribution to bearings, also reducing weight and centrifugal force. A Holset viscous-type damper is fitted at the free end of the crankshaft to control vibration and give smooth running throughout the engine speed range. Four-bolt 'I'-section forged connecting rods of nickel-chrome, machined all over and drilled for pressure lubrication of gudgeon-pins and piston cooling are used. The bearings—pre-finished—are replaceable by withdrawing the rods through the cylinder bore, and the big-end bolts are interlocked by locking discs. Timing is spur driven, a single camshaft being used for the valve gear and injection pump. Any cam can be removed without disturbing the shaft.

CAV fuel pumps mounted on the camshaft are used. These have Sulzer-type double-helix plungers, giving the feature that enables the point of injection to be advanced automatically as load and speed increase. Each pump has a fuel cut-out

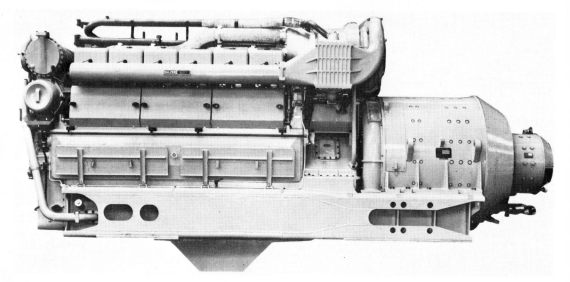

device to permit cutting-out of any one cylinder;
a regulating system prevents overloading of
remaining cylinders. The pumps are bench-
calibrated and the fuel rack stop pre-set. The
feed to the pumps is set at 30lb/sq in to ensure
cool fuel and prevent cavitation. The difference
in the 'A' and 'B' engines is the fuel pumps, the
latter having a larger diameter plunger for extra
fuel input.

The Sulzer exhaust-gas turboblower has plain
bearings and is mounted on the main generator
frame. Lubricating oil temperature is controlled
by an engine-mounted heat-exchanger through
which engine cooling water is circulated. Engine
speed is governed by a regulator controlled by a
self-lapping air valve in the driver's master controller. The governor on the engine has a servo
mechanism to drive the regulator in the main
generator separate field circuit. The output is
thereby adjusted to the correct load for the engine
speed selected by the driver. Overloading is automatically regulated when applied.

The combined pump set is motor-driven and
circulates both cooling water and lubricating oil
as well as fuel under pressure to the engine. This
set circulates oil and water when the engine is
stopped and before starting; when running,
lubricating oil circulation is mainly by an engine-
driven pump.

The 6LDA28 'A' and 'B' engines were fitted to
a total of 594 BR locomotives during the 1958-67
period.

The 8LDA28A pressure-charged engine is very
similar to the 6LDA28 but has eight cylinders,
being rated continuously at 1550bhp at 750rpm.

The one-hour rating is 1705bhp at 750rpm. The
engine has no inter-cooler. At the 1550bhp rating
the bmep is 151lb/sq in, charging pressure 14lb/
sq in over atmospheric, and specific fuel con-
sumpton 0·38lb/bhp per hour. Pistons, liners,
connecting rods and bearings are interchangeable
with those of other Sulzer engines fitted to BR
locomotives. This engine was supplied for use in
98 locomotives of Class 33 during 1960-62.

The most powerful Sulzer engine used in BR
locomotives is also the most prolific, for the
12LDA28 in its 'A', 'B' and 'C' versions was used
in 705 BR locomotives. The engine is noteworthy for its compact size for its power, this
feature being very useful to locomotive designers
with restricted space but high power demands to
meet. The engine is virtually two separate six-
cylinder engines side by side, both rotating in the
same direction, coupled by gears driving the
generator shaft in the opposite direction at
approximately 60 per cent higher speed than that
of the engine. So far as BR is concerned the initial
1955 order was followed by other large orders for
this engine, which hitherto had only been used in
35 locomotives of the SNCF at a 2000bhp rating.

Until the advent of the LVA range this engine
was the largest and most powerful in the Sulzer
rail traction range. It is of twin-bank form, with
cylinders arranged in two vertical banks of six,
each bank with its own crankshaft driving a

French-built Sulzer 16LVA24 Vee-type engine coupled to a Brush alternator group being lowered into the superstructure of the 4000bhp prototype locomotive *Kestrel* at the works of Brush at Loughborough. *(Brush Electrical Machines)*

common output shaft solidly coupled straight through spur gearing with a step-up ratio of 1 : 1·44, giving a generator speed of 1080rpm at 750rpm engine speed, and allowing a smaller generator to be employed. The main components, pistons, liners, connecting rods and bearings are identical and interchangeable with those of the aforementioned six- and eight-cylinder engines. The mean piston speed is 1760ft/min, and at 2300bhp the bmep UIC rating is 150lb/sq in with a charging pressure of 10lb/sq in above atmospheric pressure.

In common with other engines, the crankcase is an integral structure made up from a series of cast-steel transverse frames enclosed in steel plates. A cross-frame is fitted at each main bearing position and also at the output gear-bearing positions. The open box-form side plates extend to form the generator mounting, while the bottom is closed to form the crank chamber. The two crankshafts are arranged as close together as their balance weights allow, giving good water jacket space between cylinder bores and heads.

The Sulzer exhaust-gas turbo-blower, mounted on the phasing gear casing between engine and generator, is a four-entry type, two from each bank of cylinders. The initial engines had Swiss-built blowers, but de Haviland made them under licence for later engines. No inter-cooler was used on the 2300bhp 'A' version engine used in the ten BR class 44 locomotives in 1959/60.

In its 'B' version the engine gave 2500bhp at 750rpm, being provided with a small inter-cooler in addition to pressure-charging. This engine is used in 183 BR locomotives of classes 45/6 built 1960–63.

The final version, the 'C' variant, passed its UIC 100-hour test in 1962. This pressure-charged and inter-cooled engine is continuously rated at 2750bhp at 800rpm, and has a mean piston speed of 1888ft/min and a bmep of 168lb/sq in. With a step-up gear ratio of 1 : 1·44 the engine drives the generator at 1150rpm. This engine was used in 512 class 47 locomotives of BR, built 1962–68.

With the maximum output in sight for the LDA engine, Sulzer was developing its new range, the LVA24, from the mid-1950s. In this, Sulzer returned to the vee-form engine given up in 1926/7, but available again from 1960.

BR only applied the LVA24 in five of its locomotives; these were five class 47, D1702–6, built new with this engine as class 48 and operating as such 1965–71, and in addition the private prototype locomotive *Kestrel*. The LVA engine was offered in 8-, 12- and 16-cylinder models: 8LVA24, 12LVA24 and 16LVA24, all with cylinders of 9·6in × 11·2in bore/stroke. They gave 1750, 2650 and 3500bhp originally, running at 1050rpm to UIC ratings.

Only the 12- and 16-cylinder engines have been

used in the UK: the 12LVA24 at 2650bhp, and later the uprated 16LVA24 with an official rating of 4000bhp. All these engines were built in France at the Sulzer works at Mantes. The 12LVA24 engine had a bmep of 213lb/sq in and a piston speed of 1929ft/min; the 16LVA24 had a bmep of 230lb/sq in, piston speed of 2020ft/min.

The vee engine has a relatively light bedplate-crankcase built up from steel plate by welding. It carries no running gear forces. Side covers provide access for main and big-end bearings. The cylinder block is fabricated mostly by welding from steel plate, but the bearing saddles are of cast steel and welded into the structure. The cylinder block also forms the water jackets. The cylinder block takes the running forces via the cast steel/forged steel, stress-relieved bearing covers attached to it. The cylinder liners are of heat treated cast iron and are water-cooled, being sealed top and bottom from the water jacket by plastic and rubber rings respectively. Cylinder heads of heat-treated cast iron are also water-cooled and have four machined seats for the valves: two each for inlet and exhaust, plus bores for fuel injection and, if required, a valve for compressed-air starting.

Cast aluminium silicon-alloy pistons with cooling oil-circulating grooves under the crown are fitted, each piston having two chrome and copper plated compression rings, and two oil-control rings. Connecting rods are drop forgings of chrome-nickel steel machined all over, being arranged side-by-side on the crankpin for each pair of cylinders. Big-ends are parted diagonally for withdrawal upwards through the cylinder bore. Big-end bearings are of tri-metal steel, lead bronze, and a lead alloy flashed running layer. Floating gudgeon pins run in steel and lead-bronze bearings. Small-ends are of bi-metal.

Short and sturdy chrome-molybdenum steel crankshafts with hard-chromed and ground journals and crankpins are used. At 1050rpm no counter-balance weights were used, but upon increasing to 1100rpm weights to balance 38 per cent of the rotating forces were used. A Holset damper is fitted.

The fuel injection is by an individual pump for each cylinder, driven by its own cam through a roller and tappet. The camshafts, one for each bank of cylinders, are driven by chrome-nickel gears from the crankshaft, the shafts themselves being of case-hardened chrome-nickel steel with hardened journal and cam surfaces. They are assembled by bolting together separate flanged cam groups for each cylinder. The engine governor is of Sulzer design. A Sulzer exhaust-gas turbo-charger is fitted, one to the 8- and 12-cylinder engines, and two to the 16-cylinder engine. The inter-cooler is centrally-mounted between the cylinder heads.

CHAPTER 3
THE BRITISH RAIL DERBY TYPE 2—CLASSES 24 AND 25

British Railways' standard type 2, if it may be called that, is the Derby works designed and built Bo-Bo diesel-electric introduced in 1958, built to an initial Modernisation Plan pilot scheme order of 1955 for 20 locomotives. Subsequently, batches were built at Crewe and Darlington works, and also by Beyer, Peacock Gorton Ltd, so that when production ended in 1967, 478 locomotives of 1160/1250bhp had been built, numbered D5000–5299/D7500–7677.

The allocation of the design and construction to Derby works drew on that works' continuous association with diesel-electric locomotive building since 1939. This association was almost entirely with the 350/400bhp 0-6-0DE shunter, but Derby had built 10000/1, the EE-equipped 1600bhp Co-Co locomotives in 1947/8, not to mention the Fell 2-D-2 2000hp diesel-mechanical locomotive 10100. Nevertheless, the fact that Derby had done these things no doubt had some bearing.

The approach adopted in the design of the Derby type 2, hereafter referred to as class 24 or 25, was very conventional, as in fact were almost all the designs built by the UK locomotive industry. When the allocation of locomotive orders resulting from the pilot scheme was made, 33 out of 174 locomotives were allocated to BR

The first of the BR Derby type 2 1160bhp Bo-Bo locomotives of class 24/0. D5000 has the external features of the original units—cab-front corridor doors, headcode lamps and discs, and fairing at base of bodysides. The waist-height lining was only applied to this locomotive. *(GEC Traction)*

workshops. Derby received 30, 20 of 1160bhp and 10 of 2300bhp, all with Sulzer engines. The conventional design was decided upon so that railway workshops could mass-produce the type to achieve rapid replacement of steam and so that at the same time the design should be as light-weight as possible within strength, safety and durability requirements. There was no provision made for building and testing prototypes.

A twin end-cab, full-width body layout was chosen for classes 24/25, the superstructure being based on the trussed girder concept for weight and deflection resistance properties, the bridge-girder framework carrying the power equipment being able to withstand 200-ton buffing loads. The underframe consists of two main longitudinals, each made of two standard channel sections placed back-to-back. These are covered top and bottom by plates which form ducts for traction motor cooling air. The underframe carries a 16-gauge steel sealing plate to take oil, water and fuel leakages; it is sloped so that any spillage collects in two tanks. Two main transoms tie the frame members together and provide the carrying units for bogie pivots and other cross-members. The underframe longitudinals also carry the four-point engine mountings.

Bodysides are based on open-girder frames which are attached to the underframe transoms and cross-members and at the top by further cross-sections. The openings in the side frames provided location for air-intake units and radiators. On later locomotives the air intake grilles

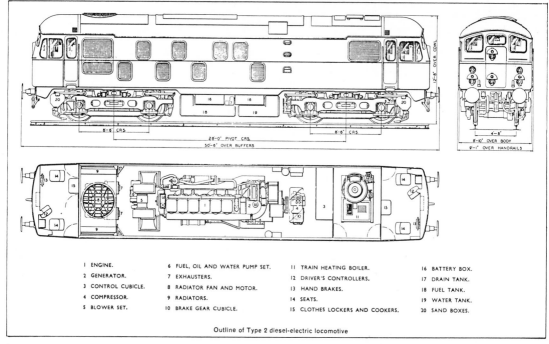

1 ENGINE.	6 FUEL, OIL AND WATER PUMP SET.	11 TRAIN HEATING BOILER.	16 BATTERY BOX.
2 GENERATOR.	7 EXHAUSTERS.	12 DRIVER'S CONTROLLERS.	17 DRAIN TANK.
3 CONTROL CUBICLE.	8 RADIATOR FAN AND MOTOR.	13 HAND BRAKES.	18 FUEL TANK.
4 COMPRESSOR.	9 RADIATORS.	14 SEATS.	19 WATER TANK.
5 BLOWER SET.	10 BRAKE GEAR CUBICLE.	15 CLOTHES LOCKERS AND COOKERS.	20 SAND BOXES.

Outline of Type 2 diesel-electric locomotive

Above: Layout diagram of D5000. Apart from details, the first 114 locomotives (D5000–5113) were built to this design mechanically.   *(GEC Traction)*

Below: Comparative side and front elevations of class 25/0 (top) 1250bhp locomotive showing first type of cab roof-mounted indicator boxes and revision of layout of bodyside air intake grilles. Class 25/2 (lower) 1250bhp locomotive with combined indicator box/ warning horn unit on cab roof, and elimination of fairing at base of bodysides.   *(British Railways)*

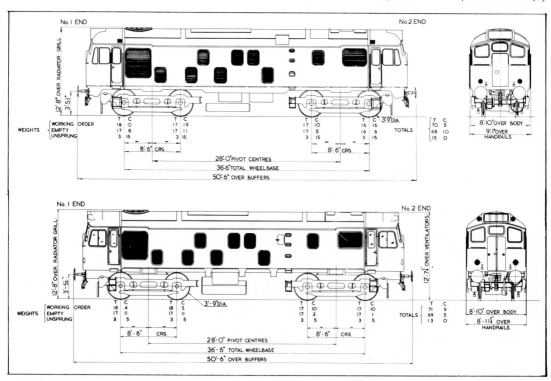

Superstructure of D5094, the first Darlington-built 1160bhp locomotive under construction at the North Road works on 15 August 1959.   *(Brian Webb)*

were repositioned at cant-rail level in line with the BRCW built locomotives of classes 26, 27 and 33, to overcome the tendency for the lower filters in the intakes to be blocked by ingress of dust.

Bufferbeams in the 24/25s are carried on two 'I' section beams, which also form part of the dragbox which carries normal buffing and draw-gear, but in common with other BR diesels, pro-vision for fitting some form of automatic couplers was made.

The roof sections between the cabs are com-pletely removeable and of specially mounted and sealed aluminium construction. Aluminium doors over the engine allow access to the engine top; the roof was left free of attached equipment on its underside. All roof sections are located by pads into the locomotive frame arranged to pro-vide extra stiffening to the body construction. The cabs are framed and covered in aluminium, but have glass-fibre roof canopies which, after the first 114 locomotives, were modified to incorporate the four-digit train indicator box.

In common with all the earlier BR type 2, 3 and 4 diesel electrics, a pair of doors in the cab fronts cover a folding gangway/corridor connec-tion to meet a requirement for inter-locomotive access when working in multiple and to allow train-heating boiler manual shut-down 15 minutes before the locomotive left the train, which some-times meant while running. After 233 loco-motives of classes 24/25 had been built, the doors were discontinued, and the cab design revised internally and externally. Since then many of the locomotives with the gangways have had them removed and the doors welded up. Apart from the gangway doors, all doors in these loco-motives are aluminium castings.

The bogies, despite their appearance, are simple box-frame units akin to railway carriage practice of the period. They are outside-framed units of welded and riveted construction with a spring-plank bolster arrangement and four spring links. Coil springs are used for bolster and axle-boxes, the latter in conjunction with an equalis-ing beam and hydraulic shock absorbers. The frame is fabricated from three welded assemblies, two side frames and one centre cross-member, plus the headstocks. The side frames are light and only $\frac{1}{4}$in thick. They are made wider in the centre to accommodate bolster springs, and are deep enough for the spring cross-beam.

Of the first batch of 20 locomotives, ten were fitted with Athermos plain-bearing, pressure-lubricated axleboxes rather similar to the Iso-thermos type used by Armstrong Whitworth in the 1930s, and the remainder with SKF roller-bearing boxes.

Special care was reputedly taken with brake rigging design so as to limit time spent in brake block adjusting and changing. Brake equipment is by Davies & Metcalfe and is of Oerlikon type with Westinghouse and Davies & Metcalfe brake cylinders. The locomotive is air-braked and originally only vacuum for train braking was provided. However, the change to train air-braking has necessitated installation of an addi-tional air compressor, considerably impeding inside access in the process. Air compressors by Davies & Metcalfe or Westinghouse are used, vacuum coming from two Westinghouse or Northey Reavell exhausters, the latter being fitted originally on locomotives D5233–99/7500–97. Anti-slip brakes are fitted.

Internal layout of classes 24/25 involves three compartments between the cabs. The largest area is occupied by the engine/generator set, together with control cubicle, compressor and traction motor blower set. At each end are the train-heating boiler compartment and radiator com-partment.

The engine is a pressure-charged Sulzer 6LDA28 six-cylinder unit giving 1160bhp in its 'A' version and 1250bhp in its 'B' version incor-porating charge-air cooling. Both run at 750rpm. Engine cooling incorporates self-draining radia-tors with frost protection. The roof-mounted cooling fan is electrically driven and thermo-statically controlled according to water tempera-ture. All air entering the engine room is filtered through Air Maze units.

Considerable variation exists in these loco-motives' electrical equipment. D5000–49 have the British Thompson Houston (BTH) generator, comprising a single-bearing 12-pole type with separate belt-driven excitation and self-ventila-tion. It is a 735Kw machine rated at 750/525V,

980/140A at 750rpm. Included also is an eight-pole separately excited auxiliary generator of constant voltage rated at 55Kw, 110V, at 500/700rpm. This machine is recessed into the main generator commutator. The exciter is a four-pole machine with self, separate and differential series excitation windings. This is mounted above the auxiliary generator, being belt driven from it. D5000–49 have main generator output controlled by the engine load regulator operating in a rheostat in the exciter separate field.

All remaining class 24 and 25 locomotives have no exciter, the main generator having separate, shunt and differential windings with load control in the separate field. However, a further difference concerns the first 25 class 25 1250bhp locomotives, D5151–75, which have a main generator rating of 750/545V, 1090/1500A, the remainder being 780/545V, 1050/1500A.

There are four axle-hung traction motors which are nose-suspended on chevron Metalastik rubber mountings. The whole of class 24, D5000–D5150, and D5151–75 of class 25 have the earlier motor of BTH type 137BY and 137BX respectively. This motor gives 222hp at 525V, 350A, at 560rpm on the class 24, and 245hp at 545V, 375A, in the class 25. All these locomotives have their motors connected permanently in parallel. Gear ratios vary. For D5000–D5150 the ratio is 16:81, for and D5151-75 18:79. The first 151 locomotives were designed for 75mph maximum, but the remainder were increased to 90mph. All the remaining locomotives of class 25, D5176–D5299 and D7500–D7677, are of 1250bhp and have the Associated Electrical Industries (AEI) type 253AY traction motor rated at 234hp, 315V, 650A, at 460rpm connected in series parallel pairs. These motors have a bonded rubber and steel sandwich suspension unit.

The traction motors are series wound and drive through single-reduction spur gearing of resilient type to cushion mechanical shocks while running on irregular trackwork and during acceleration. Traction motor blowers provide force ventilation, one for each bogie, being driven by an AEI 12·2hp 110V motor running at 2600rpm.

These locomotives are not being fitted with electric train heating (eth), while many are without steam generators, in which case concrete ballast weights are carried to equalise axle loadings. Where fitted, the Stone-Vapor steam generator is used as standard in both classes.

Considerable variation in service weights results. The main fuel tank is slung from the underframe and fits around the battery boxes, which are arranged for running out on rails for servicing. Water tanks are both underslung and in the heating boiler compartment.

Changes in external appearance due to discontinuation of fitting cab gangway doors, fitting roof-mounted four-digit indicator boxes, and the adoption of the bodyside design based on the BRCW-built locomotives of classes 26 and 27 cause some confusion.

The first 151 locomotives of class 24 have the following variations: original body style, front gangway, no indicator boxes—D5000–D5113. D5114–50 are similar, but have indicator boxes. All the class 24s up to D5113 had a hinged, shaped vallance or fairing along the bottom edge of the body side. Due to wear and poor maintenance this was later removed and not fitted to subsequent locomotives.

Class 25 has the following variations: original body style, front gangways and roof-mounted indicator boxes—D5151–D5232/D7568–97; new body style without front gangways, but with roof indicator boxes—D5233–99/D7500–67/D7598–D7677. Due to accident damage and transfer of locomotive cabs between batches, some hybrid variants are found. Some of these appear in

Class 24 Speed/tractive effort curves.

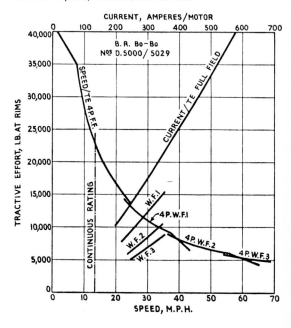

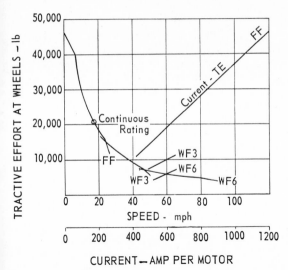

Class 25 Speed/tractive effort curves.

accompanying illustrations. Reference to locomotive list tables indicates sequence of construction.

D5299 was earmarked for fitting with the up-rated and revised Sulzer 6LDA28-R engine of 1750bhp. This engine was developed and tested at Winterthur and had a four-valve cylinder head in a strengthened engine. Two prototypes were built but abandoned in 1965 in view of LVA24 developments. One engine went to Zurich University and that in the UK went into standby generator set employment in the West Country. D5299 appeared as a standard locomotive some 12 months after its numerical neighbours.

D5008 was used on an extensive testing programme from Derby in 1959, which is covered in detail in BR Testing Bulletin No. 21. Static and running tests were done. Tests in the latter case were with the mobile testing units on the Toton–Leicester–Rugby–Market Harborough–Derby–Toton route at constant speeds with fixed engine and control notch settings of 330, 400, 450, 500, 550, 650 and 750rpm. Records of track speed, drawbar pull and fuel consumption were made, together with records of all aspects of traction equipment. Variable speed tests were made on the steep Toton–Derby–Chesterfield–Chapel en le Frith–Peak Forest–Ambergate–Butterley–Toton route. A 560-ton load of coaching stock and dynamometer car was hauled a total of 4200 miles. D5008 was found able to use its full engine output between 9·3 and 58·3mph. Maximum

tractive effort of 40,000lb at 22·3 per cent adhesion was recorded, while the continuous tractive effort of 22,700lb was more than the calculated figure.

All the Sulzer-engined locomotives on BR come into the 'Blue Star' coupling code for multiple-unit operation of up to three locomotives of similar make or otherwise. The original proposal was made in 1955 by the then British Transport Commission (BTC) that all diesel-electric locomotives, regardless of make, should be able to operate in multiple within the speed range of the slower unit. Not all UK locomotive builders were ready for this, so the idea was temporarily dropped. A 110V control was required and, as the initial pilot scheme locomotive orders for 174 diesels involved seven manufacturers—ie, diesel engine, electrical equipment and brake equipment—the problem was of some magnitude. In the event, EE had evolved a pneumatic speed control for BR locomotive 10203, while Sulzer had developed a similar system in Switzerland which had been used on locomotives built by BRCW exported from the UK. Consultations between BTC, EE, Sulzer, BTH and CP/Allen West indicated the possibility of a common scheme. The use of a painted 'Blue Star' symbol on the front of each locomotive identified its suitability for coupling to other similarly-marked locomotives. Other locomotives not within this scheme were coded 'Red Circle'. To operate in multiple, locomotives must be controllable in the following systems from the leading locomotive cab:

(a) Engine starting and stopping
(b) Engine speed and output
(c) Electric power control including reversing and notching
(d) Auxiliary machines
(e) Equipment protective devices
(f) Fault indication
(g) Brake system.

The 6LDA28 and 8LDA28 engines are more sturdy and certainly less troublesome than the twin-bank 12LDA28 engine. They have suffered failures of welds in the engine structure, but these were minor compared to those of their larger brethren. BR attended to the repairs by welding and stress relieving. Cylinder liners, transition rubbers, cylinder-head core plugs do leak coolant, but do not cause so much trouble as these locomotives are not usually worked 'flat out' like larger locomotives. Fuel starvation resulting in loss of power caused by blocked filter elements occurs on some locomotives. Some trouble has been experienced with fractures of the turbo-charger water jackets on the 6LDA28, and particularly the 8LDA28 engines fitted to class 33. Coolant starvation, due probably to air-locks formed while topping-up the system, was thought the cause, while air-locks when refilling a class 25 system were common. The 6LDA28 engines in their 'A' form had their crankcase doors secured by $\frac{1}{2}$in Whitworth studs and nuts round their periphery, but 'B' engines have doors with six knobs in their centre line. Both variants had folding platforms attached to their beds for the engine fitters to stand on, but these were removed when the new explosion relief valves of BICERA type were fitted (see chapter 6) to the doors.

Exhaust silencing of the earlier locomotives of classes 24 and 25 caused some serious fires and explosions in the expansion box. The exhaust gases from the turbo-charger were ducted into the expansion box fitted in a roof-well over the brake equipment frame, but as the engine crank-

case breather was also piped into this box, the slight carry-over of oil and vapour caused ignition at times, with costly consequences. The expansion box and silencer were later eliminated, and a short straight-out exhaust stack fitted. Exhaust silencing is now only provided by its passage through the turbo-charger.

On the 6LDA28 engines, cylinder blocks and crankcases are identical, but the 6LDA28A engine of 1160bhp has its own cylinder heads, fuel pumps and fuel injectors.

The mechanical portions have given few problems, one of the main ones being the vibration which sets up in those class 24s with aluminium portions of bodywork. The underframes always bend downwards in head-on collisions, suggesting some design weaknesses.

The cabs, due to the provision of the cab-front corridors in earlier locomotives, resulted in the driver being cramped into the left-hand side of the cab. Elimination of the corridor resulted in a revised cab design. Locomotives D5000–D5175 had their cabs panelled with aluminium sections internally. While good for maintenance due to screw fixings, the draughts while running provoked many complaints from the footplate men, so that in common with all such cabs on BR all such joints were covered with masking tape—an

Exchange of cabs between withdrawn and damaged locomotives resulted in a number of hybrids. Class 24/1 24 055, formerly D5055, has the cabs from later locomotive D5114, withdrawn in October 1972. Note fitted but blanked-off indicator box, retention of headcode lights and discs, and welding up of corridor doors. Stoke Cockshute, June 1975.   *(Fred Kerr)*

Three variants at Stoke Cockshute depot in June 1975. Left to right: 25/2 25 145 in correct condition, 24/1 24 142 with cab roof indicator and horn arrangement of classes 25/2 and 25/3, and corridor doors welded-up, and 24/1 24 082 in original form, apart from removal of bodyside fairing and welding up of corridor doors.   (Fred Kerr)

untidy but effective solution. All the BR-built class 24/25 locomotives are prone to rain entry due to poor body and roof joints, and poor panel work when built; by far the best are the class 25/3 locomotives D7624–59 which were built by Beyer, Peacock Gorton Ltd.

The introduction of dual-braking systems meant finding space for the additional air compressor in locomotives fitted with train-heating boilers. This was fitted on the A side of the locomotive, restricting internal access, so that bodyside filters on that side had to be provided with external access doors, B side remaining as before.

After the severe winters of 1963/4, the large bodyside grilles alongside the train-heating boiler were fitted with blanking plates in an attempt to prevent the boiler freezing.

Auxiliary machine layout is poor, causing considerable difficulty at depots. On vacuum-braked locomotives, the traction motor blower motor is at the free end of the diesel engine above the combined pump set. To get this out, it has to be turned round and manhandled through the B side of the engine room to reach a triangular hatch in the bodyside. The air-compressor is at the main generator end, and once out of the engine room, has to be taken out of the side window in No. 2 cab, the exhausters too having to gain exit by a similar process from No. 1 cab, as the doorways are too narrow.

Cab equipment variations are many. Originally some locomotives had handbrake position indicators; these are now being discarded. The driver's console or desk varies in style and construction, and some later locomotives with the redesigned cab, classes 25/2 and 25/3, have AEI electronic speedometers which control the field-weakening of the traction motors, and electronic mileage recorders. Earlier batches have the axle-driven mileage recorder mounted on the axlebox cover.

Electrical problems have not been large, but from the maintenance viewpoint the BTH main generator fitted to earlier locomotives have brush boxes on a ring which can slide round the commutator; these often proved difficult to move, so that the fitter was forced to examine the bottom boxes by crawling about in the engine drip tray. On the AEI version, the brush boxes can be pulled round the commutator by a chain-driven device, so easing access.

The AEI type 253AY traction motor fitted to the majority of class 25 is easier to work on than the BTH motor, the former being smaller and very compact, this being especially appreciated when changing the brake blocks.

Prolonged AEI 253AY traction motor troubles with class 25/2 variants were highlighted in 1972 when the Western Region, due to the withdrawal of diesel-hydraulic locomotives, had recently received its first Sulzer locomotives of class 25. In the early summer of that year a spate of failures on the 63 miles Port Talbot–Ebbw Vale run with class 25s in multiple on iron ore trains was investigated. The route was an easy one, with only the six miles Aberbeeg–Ebbw Vale section, which has a ruling gradient of 1 in 80, and a restart at Aberbeeg, providing any difficulty. The use of two 25s in multiple-unit resulted in traction motor overheating on this section and train loadings were reduced from 990 to 900, and then to 810 tons, at which point the problem ceased.

On 16 June 1972 locomotives 7676 (class 25/3),

with electronic control of field divert contactors by road speed, and 7569 (class 25/2), with conventional engine/generator controlled field divert contactors, made this run with 18 wagons and a load of 810 tons. Figures obtained indicated that 7569 was taking more than half the load. In early October further tests, with 7569 leading, showed that 7676 as train engine did most work! 7569 was found to be using traction motor current slightly above the one-hour rating, and diverting at 22mph; 7676 was diverting at 29mph. As balancing speed was mainly between these two speeds, 7569 was found to be carrying 100/150A more per traction motor than 7676. The outcome was that it was considered to be variations in equipment, notably the field divert relays, and their poor adjustment which caused this problem. Other factors included variations in traction motor cooling due to the blowers being faulty or incorrectly maintained, diesel engines putting out too high bhp due to governor changing, load regulator switches failing in closed position and causing current fluctuations, and excessive motor current. The AEI 253AY traction motor has a continuous rating very close to its one-hour rating, no overloads being fitted.

During 1975 the LMR changed 66 AEI253 traction motors at its depots, this rising in 1976 to 121 motors, of which, on 11 locomotives, all four motors were changed. One of the main causes was inter-pole coil failure. This was not solely a traction motor problem, as it involved control gear also, and it was decided to fit an EE type field-divert relay used in EE locomotives of BR classes 20 and 40 and adapt this for use in class 25. The field-divert contactor was to be re-designed and attention to the field-divert resistor recommended. In 1976 it was agreed to do trials with a class 25/2 locomotive, 25088 being selected, with its main generator altered to class 25/3 characteristics. This was on trial in 1977.

The shortage of spare components is a common factor in keeping BR locomotives out of traffic. With class 25 this has been particularly bad in the area of turbo-chargers and traction motor armatures. In any ageing diesel fleet, corrosion presents problems and there has been heavy expenditure on class 25, notably on cab sub-floors and on the bodyside lower edge between the cabs. Cab removal, fitting of new sub-floor and cabside support angles was resorted to. If two were done on one locomotive the combined cost exceeded the BR financial limit on locomotives damaged in accidents. Only loco-

motives with a 'life expectancy of after 1983' were to be done in view of this.

At the end of 1976 the classes 24 and 25 were achieving average BR availabilities of 88·6 and 78·5 per cent, the regional figures being: LMR, 88·6 for class 24 and 25; the Scottish Region, 72·5; and WR, 87·5 for class 25.

The withdrawal of locomotives of class 24 has eased to some extent the spares situation for most of the 6LDA28-powered BR classes, as all re-usable parts are removed, leaving only the shell of the locomotive for scrapping. Withdrawal of class 24 started in 1969, due to examples being uneconomic to repair. D5000/1/5/10/19 43/93 were in this category. After periods in store the majority were returned to traffic, surviving until withdrawal commenced in 1975.

Many instances of minor and severe collisions and fires have occurred in these classes, and in some cases withdrawal followed. Typical of the more severe ones was that involving D5122, which was cut up at Cowlairs works in 1971 after involvement in a collision and fire with a railcar set at Castlecary in August 1968. D7605 on the 06.30 Liverpool–Nottingham parcels on 16 December 1971 collided with class 20s D8115/42 on a Derby–Bestwood freight at Lenton South Junction, and was scrapped at Derby in 1972. D5278, involved in a head-on single-line collision near Great Rocks, Derbyshire, was withdrawn in May 1971 and cut-up by a scrap dealer at Peak Forest in October. Chester proved to be treacherous for the class, for on 8 May 1972, D5028 ran out of control with an Ellesmere Port–Mold Junction oil tanker train and derailed in Chester General Station; it was burnt out in the process, withdrawn in June, and cut up at Crewe. The other Chester accident was the spectacular runaway iron ore train with a class 47 which, on 9 July 1969, was diverted into Chester diesel depot, demolishing locomotives D5043/93/138/9. They were withdrawn in August 1969.

The value of diesel locomotives as traffic and crowd-pulling machines is dawning on our so-called steam preservation lines. The North Yorkshire Moors Railway had class 24 24032 (D5032) on hire from a Stockton-on-Tees scrap merchant, T. and J. Thompson & Co. Ltd, in 1976/77. It is to be hoped that a class 25 will be kept for the National Railway Museum at York, where its inclusion could well supplant the class 31 (D5500) without its original engine, which at present represents the BR type 2 diesel-electric locomotive in the collection.

D5010 on loan to the SR from the LMR and seen on a down boat train at Sandling Junction in September 1964. This locomotive was one of the ten of the first batch fitted with 'Athermos' axleboxes. Note standard broad band lining at base of body adopted as standard with the green livery. *(Derek Cross)*

Construction of D5000 started at Derby works in the autumn of 1957; it finally appeared at Marylebone station on 24 July 1958 for official inspection. All the first 20 locomotives were for the LMR, but following trials with D5000 between Derby and Millers Dale, and then on Derby–Manchester–Liverpool passenger duties— and in spite of allocation to Crewe depot but on loan to Derby—plans were announced to send 15 locomotives to the SR until its own diesel locomotives were delivered.

From early 1959 the SR South Eastern division started to receive locomotives and to train drivers but the SR Civil Engineer, upset by the locomotives' five tons overweight, decreed weight reduction by removal of train-heating boilers and other fittings. Even then their route availability was restricted. They were all allocated to Hither Green depot and sent to Eastleigh works for heavy repairs. Movement to and fro saw D5008 return to the LMR in May 1959 for testing, while in 1960 some train-heating boilers were refitted at Derby.

On the SR the locomotives worked all types of duties, though mostly freight in winter due to lack of heating equipment. They even operated on Continental boat-train services and the Golden Arrow. When delivery of the SR class 33

1550bhp BRCW-Sulzers began in 1960/1, their lack of steam-heating, being only eth-fitted, and the shortage of eth-fitted stock, saw the SR class 24 then refitted with boilers, working in multiple with them to provide train heating. In 1962 the locomotives were on Southampton–Nine Elms freights, and inter-regional, cross-London freights. During 1962 the locomotives returned to the LMR.

Deliveries from Derby and Crewe during 1959/ 60 resulted in the influx of the class 24 to the ER and NER. Allocations were to March, Ipswich and Stratford on the GE lines, D5020–9/66–75 coming from Derby and D5030–65/76–93 from Crewe. Darlington works built D5094/5 for the ER, and D5096–D5113 for the NER. NER locomotives went to Gateshead depot but were initially based at South Gosforth multiple-unit depot. Local trips to Carlisle and in Northumberland were followed by trips to Edinburgh, and by summer 1960 workings on Newcastle–Leeds locals and summer Saturday trains to Scarborough and Carlisle were undertaken; in the latter case the overnight Stranraer boat train was their duty. D5094 was tried at Finsbury Park in November 1960 and was successful on cross-London freights from Ferme Park to the SR at Hither Green and Feltham. In early 1961 more were drafted in and fitted at Stratford works with trip-cocks on their braking system to allow their use over the London Transport widened lines.

Further NER batches were D5147–50 and D5151–82, the latter the first class 25s, and came from Derby and Darlington for allocation to

Above: D5181 of class 25/1 takes single-handed a Tyne Dock–Consett iron ore train past Hedworth Lane box on 16 August 1968. *(Ian S. Carr)*

Below: A brand new Beyer, Peacock Gorton Ltd built 25/3 D7625 at Scarborough awaiting departure on a summer Saturday train to Sheffield on 21 August 1965. The two-tone green livery adopted for locomotives of the final body style is ably demonstrated here.

(Brian Webb)

Gateshead, Thornaby and Leeds (Holbeck) depots. By this time they were familiar sights on the East Coast mine line (ECML). Transfers took some to York in early 1963, by which time Thornaby locomotives were working many other depots' former steam locomotive turns.

One of the greatest losses to the steam enthusiast was the takeover by Gateshead locomotives of the Tyne Dock–Consett iron ore trains in the summer of 1966, displacing the BR class 9F 2-10-0s. For this work extra air-compressors were fitted for operation of the wagon door air-system. The locomotives usually worked in multiple on these trains.

In October 1965 ER and NER allocations for classes 24 and 25 were:

Ipswich	D5036–49
Finsbury Park	D5050–72/94/5
Sheffield (Tinsley)	D7624–54
York	D5096/8/100/76
Thornaby	D5151–75
Gateshead	D5097, D5101–13/47–50, D5077–82

Tinsley had received its allocation in 1965, being part of the D7624–49 batch which worked from various local depots and were built by Beyer, Peacock Gorton Ltd (BPG). This firm received an order for 54 locomotives numbered D7624–77 in 1964 in its effort to keep part of the

Below: Side and front elevation of the final development of the Derby type 2 in its class 25/3 form. Whilst retaining the cab adopted for later class 25/2, it had the bodyside design based on that of BRCW built locomotives of classes 26, 27 and 33, D7500–67/98–7677 being class 25/3; however the final batches of 25/2, D5233–99, had the same bodyside design also.

(British Railways)

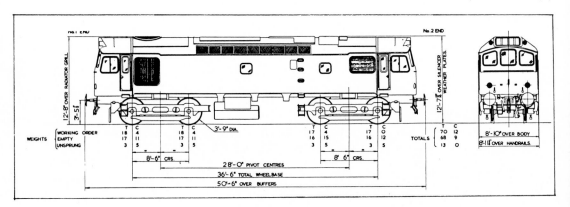

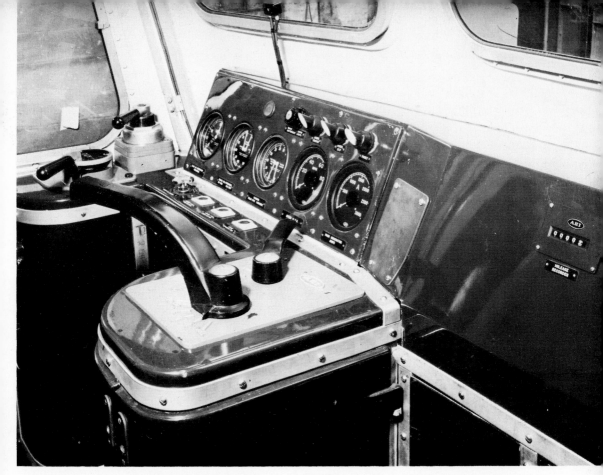

Above: Elimination of the cab corridor arrangement enabled the somewhat restricted cab layout to be completely revised in classes 25/2 and 25/3. The cab of a Beyer, Peacock Gorton built locomotive ably illustrates this. It is equipped with AEI electronic speedometer and mileage recorder.   *(GEC Traction)*

massive Gorton Foundry, by then devoid of its staple Beyer-Garratt steam work, employed. In the event, just as its 'Hymek' diesel hydro-mechanical locomotive for BR fell out of favour, the gamble to buy time in the hope of further diesel orders failed, and Beyer, Peacock asked to be relieved of the D7660–77 batch to enable them to cut its losses and close down the locomotive business. Much trouble surrounded the placing of an order with a private builder for a design of locomotive which had previously only been built in BR works, and the transfer of some jigs to Beyer, Peacock from BR works caused some union 'blacking' of items in transit. The excellent workmanship of the BPG-built class 25s has given rise to their being called the best of the class.

At the time of writing no locomotives of classes 24 or 25 are allocated to the ER. The LMR has by far the largest allocation of these locomotives, but did not receive new locomotives until the autumn of 1960. The LMR batches comprised D5133–46/86–D5222, D7568–77, D5233–99, D7500–67 and D7670–7—built at Derby, 1960–7; D5183–5/D5223–32, D7578–97—from Darlington in 1963/4; and D7650–9—from BPG in 1966. Inter-regional transfers, as with other originally allocated batches, considerably upset the arrangement and LMR depots such as Toton, Longsight, Willesden, Crewe, Cricklewood, Carlisle (Kingmoor) and Springs Branch (Wigan) have the main allocatio.ıs.

Willesden locomotives worked on Euston outer suburban duties, replacing the 2-6-4Ts. Some were sub-allocated to Rugby where they took on Birmingham trains, Norwich trains and Euston–Rugby locals in 1960. The 1960/1 period saw multiple operation on Luton–Bonnybridge car trains, and on the 'Condor' prototype 'Freightliner' trains. By mid-1963, in common with other Sulzer locomotives, the LMR Midland Division was largely dieselised on the freight side of its traffic by the class 25s.

In October 1965 the classes 24/25 were allocated as follows on the LMR:

Midland Line: D5184–8/90–2/4/6/8/9/

Above: The LMR Midland Division is the vogue of class 25s in multiple. Here 25/3 25 180 and 25 176 rumble through Bedford with an Acton–Wellingborough freight in September 1975. *(Fred Kerr)*

Below: Class 24/1 locomotive with roof-mounted indicator boxes and cab-front headlights in welded-up corridor doors, also with small snowploughs. D5119 blowing off steam from its train-heating boiler alongside Dornoch Firth with the 11.25 Wick–Inverness in April 1973. *(Peter W. Robinson)*

A cement train at Truro on the WR with class 25/2
25 227 on 2 September 1976.　　*(Norman E. Preedy)*

D5200/1/3–7/9–12/22/4/5/7–31/5/7/40–2/4/
54/83/5–8/90–3, D7515–7/68/9/72–6/9/80/
4/8–93/5/7
London (Cricklewood): D5213–21, D7503/41
Leicester: D5189, D5248–52/5/8/69/73/89,
D7512/4/22/36/7/51
Nottingham: D5208/38/53/6/7/9–65/7/8/
70–2/80/2/94–7/9, D7500–2/4–7/9–11/3/21/
3–35/8–40/2–50/2–4/6–61/71/7/8/81/3/94
Willesden: D5008/17/24/5/7–35/73–81/3–93/
143
Camden: D5007/9/15/6/8–23/6/140/1
Bletchley: D5000/2/3/5/10/1
Rugby: D5001/4/6/12–4/144/5
Saltley: D5183/93/7/D5202/23/6/32–4/6/9/43/
5–7/66/81/4/98, D7508/18–20/70/82/5/7/96
Crewe: D5082/133
Longsight: D5134–9/42/6
Trafford Park: D5274–9, D7586

At the time of writing the survivors of class 24,
are at Crewe depot because of their steam-heating
facilities which their class 25 replacements either
do not have at all, or if they do it is not reliable.
During 1976 the above were frequently used on
the Crewe–Shrewsbury night mail service, and
even in 1977 they still appeared on some Cambrian line duties and excursion trains.

In Scotland, a prolific user of Sulzer locomotives, only two new batches were originally
delivered: class 24 D5114–32 in 1960, and class
25 D7611–23 in 1966, all from Derby works. The
first batch spent most time at Inverness where
they acquired twin headlights in their front gangway doors for Highland section workings. The
second batch went to Eastfield, working duties of
such depots as Ayr, Hurlford and Dumfries, and
with class 26 replacing many steam locomotives.
Although in October 1965 all the Scottish locomotives were based at Inverness, the principal
depots to have classes 24/25 in later years were
Polmadie, Haymarket, Eastfield and Inverness.

Class 25 in Scotland has not been very common on passenger work except for summer
Saturday reliefs, although latterly its use had
increased, notably on light Glasgow, Oban and
Dundee trains. There was also a brief and in-
glorious spell on Edinburgh–Glasgow push-and-
pull trains.

The WR resisted the class 25 until 1971, when
withdrawal of North British class 22 1000/
1100bhp diesel-hydraulics, along with others,
necessitated some inter-regional juggling, with
the result that class 25s were soon at work in
South Wales, Bristol and the West of England.
They were allocated to Newport, Bristol and
Plymouth Laira for use on mixed duties, but
mainly freight and parcels trains. In 1977 they
were on Crewe–Cardiff via Hereford services,
and on West Country local passenger trains, but
perhaps most noteworthy in multiple unit on
Penzance–Plymouth trains.

In spite of their problems the class 25 seems
set to become one of the classic BR diesel types
and their characteristic 6LDA28 throaty exhaust
clatter can be heard virtually throughout the
land from Land's End to John O'Groats.

TABLE 2 MAIN VARIATIONS IN CLASSES 24 AND 25 Bo-Bo DIESEL ELECTRICS, BASED ON BRITISH RAIL DIAGRAM BOOK MT25 OF 1974

Number series	24 001–24 049	24 001–24 049	24 001–24 049	24 050–24 150	24 050–24 150	25 001–25 025
Former number series	D5000–D5049	D5000–D5049	D5000–D5049	D5050–D5150	D5050–D5150	D5151–D5175
Class	24/0	24/0	24/0	24/1	24/1	25/0
Diagram number	24aV	24bV	24cV	241aV	241bV	25aV
Weight in working order	79ton 16cwt	78ton 14cwt	77ton 0cwt	73ton 0cwt	71ton 0cwt	70ton 5cwt
Fuel capacity, gal	546	546	546	500	500	500
Water capacity, gal	600	600	450	450	—	—
Generator type	RTB15656	RTB15656	RTB15656	RTB15656	RTB15656	RTB15656
Traction motor type	137BY	137BY	137BY	137BY	137BY	137BX
Rail hp	843	843	843	843	843	949
Maximum tractive effort, lb	40,000	40,000	40,000	40,000	40,000	39,000
Continuous tractive effort, lb/mph	21,300/14·8	21,300/14·8	21,300/14·8	21,300/14·8	21,300/14·8	20,800/17·1
Train heating boiler type (Stone Vapor)	OK4616A OK4616B	OK4616B	L4610	L4610	—	—
Braking { Locomotive / Train	A V	A V	A V	A V	A V	A V

For full details of individual locomotive renumbering see Table No. 4.

TABLE 3
BUILDING WORKS AND DATES INTO RUNNING STOCK FOR CLASS 24 AND 25 Bo-Bo DIESEL ELECTRIC LOCOMOTIVES

Number	Builder	Works No.	Date	Region
D5000	Derby	P	9/58	LM
D5001	Derby	P	11/58	LM
D5002–4	Derby	P	13/58	LM
D5005/6	Derby	P	1/59	LM
D5007	Derby	P	2/59	LM
D5008–10	Derby	P	3/59	LM
D5011–3	Derby	P	4/59	LM
D5014	Derby	P	5/59	LM
D5015–7	Derby	P	6/59	LM
D5018/9	Derby	P	7/59	LM
D5020/1	Derby		8/59	E
D5022/3	Derby		9/59	E
D5024–7	Derby		10/59	E
D5028/9	Derby		11/59	E
D5030/1	Crewe		6/59	E
D5032	Crewe		7/59	E
D5033	Crewe		8/59	E
D5034	Crewe		9/59	E
D5035	Crewe		8/59	E
D5036–9	Crewe		9/59	E
D5040	Crewe		10/59	E
D5041	Crewe		9/59	E
D5042–4	Crewe		10/59	E
D5045	Crewe		11/59	E

Number	Builder	Works No.	Date	Region
D5046	Crewe		10/59	E
D5047/8	Crewe		11/59	E
D5049	Crewe		4/60	E
D5050	Crewe		11/59	E
D5051–7	Crewe		12/59	E
D5058	Crewe		1/60	E
D5059	Crewe		12/59	E
D5060–4	Crewe		1/60	E
D5065	Crewe		2/60	E
D5066–8	Derby		12/59	E
D5069/70	Derby		1/60	E
D5071/2	Derby		2/60	E
D5073–5	Derby		3/60	E
D5076–9	Crewe		2/60	E
D5080–2	Crewe		3/60	E
D5083/4	Crewe		4/60	E
D5085/6	Crewe		5/60	E
D5087–91	Crewe		6/60	E
D5092/3	Crewe		7/60	E
D5094	Darlington		2/60	E
D5095	Darlington		3/60	E
D5096	Darlington		4/60	NE
D5097/8	Darlington		5/60	NE
D5099/100	Darlington		6/60	NE
D5101/2	Darlington		7/60	NE
D5103/4	Darlington		8/60	NE
D5105/6	Darlington		9/60	NE
D5107/8	Darlington		10/60	NE

25 001–25 025	25 026–25 082	25 026–25 082	25 083–25 149	25 083–25 149	25218–25 247	25 218–25 247	25 150–25 217	25 248–25 327
D5151–D5175	D5176–D5232	D5176–D5232	D5233–D5299	D5233–D5299	D7568–D7597	D7568–D7597	D7500–D7567	D7598–D7677
25/0	25/1	25/1	25/2	25/2	25/2	25/2	25/3	25/3
25bV	25 1aV	25 1bV	25 2aV	25 2bV	25 2cX	25 2dV	25 3aV	25 3bV
72ton 7cwt	73ton 15cwt	71ton 9cwt	73ton 1cwt	70ton 14cwt	74ton 8cwt	73ton 15cwt	70ton 14cwt	70ton 12cwt
500	500	500	500	500	500	500	500	500
—	580	—	580	—	580	580	—	—
RTB15656	RTB15656	RTB15656	RTB15656	RTB15656	RTB15656	RTB15656	RTB15656	RTB15656
137BX	253AY	253AY	253AY	253AY	253AY	253AY	153AY	253AY
949	949	949	949	949	949	949	949	949
39,000	45,000	45,000	45,000	45,000	45,000	45,000	45,000	45,000
20,800/17·1	20,800/17·1	20,800/17·1	20,800/17·1	20,800/17·1	20,800/17·1	20,800/17·1	20,800/17·1	20,800/17·1
—	L4610	—	L4610	—	L4610	L4610	—	—
A V	A V	A V	A V	A V	SA AA AA ACV	A V	A V	SA AA AA ACV

Number	Builder	Works No.	Date	Region
D5109–11	Darlington		11/60	NE
D5112	Darlington		12/60	NE
D5113	Darlington		1/61	NE
D5114	Derby		P 4/60	Sc
D5115–8	Derby		P 5/60	Sc
D5119–22	Derby		P 6/60	Sc
D5123–5	Derby		P 7/60	Sc
D5126–8	Derby		P 8/60	Sc
D5129/30	Derby		P 9/60	Sc
D5131/2	Derby		P10/60	Sc
D5133–5	Derby		P10/60	LM
D5136–40	Derby		P11/60	LM
D5141–4	Derby		P12/60	LM
D5145/6	Derby		P13/60	LM
D5147/8	Derby		12/60	NE
D5149/50	Derby		1/61	NE
D5151	Darlington		4/61	NE
D5152–4	Darlington		5/61	NE
D5155/6	Darlington		6/61	NE
D5157–9	Darlington		7/61	NE
D5160	Darlington		8/61	NE
D5161–3	Darlington		9/61	NE
D5164/5	Darlington		10/61	NE
D5166/7	Darlington		11/61	NE
D5168–70	Darlington		12/61	NE
D5171/2	Darlington		2/62	NE
D5173/4	Darlington		3/62	NE
D5175	Darlington		4/62	NE
D5176	Darlington		1/63	NE
D5177–80	Darlington		2/63	NE
D5181/2	Darlington		3/63	NE
D5183	Darlington		P 4/63	LM
D5184	Darlington		P 5/63	LM
D5185	Darlington		P 6/63	LM
D5186–8	Derby		P 3/63	LM
D5189–90	Derby		P 4/63	LM
D5191–9	Derby		P 5/63	LM
D5200–5	Derby		P 6/63	LM
D5206–14	Derby		P 7/63	LM
D5215	Derby		P 8/63	LM
D5216	Derby		P 7/63	LM
D5217–9	Derby		P 8/63	LM
D5220	Derby		P10/63	LM
D5221	Derby		P 9/63	LM
D5222	Derby		P10/63	LM
D5223	Darlington		P 7/63	LM
D5224/5	Darlington		P 8/63	LM
D5226/7	Darlington		P 9/63	LM
D5228/9	Darlington		P10/63	LM
D5230	Darlington		P11/63	LM
D5231	Darlington		P13/63	LM
D5232	Darlington		P12/63	LM
D5233–9	Derby		P13/63	LM
D5240–6	Derby		P 1/64	LM
D5247–52	Derby		P 2/64	LM
D5253–8	Derby		P 3/64	LM

Number	Builder	Works No.	Date	Region	Number	Builder	Works No.	Date	Region
D5259–64	Derby		P 4/64	LM	D7647–9	Beyer Peacock	8057–9	4/66	E
D5265–70	Derby		P 5/64	LM	D7650–2	Beyer Peacock	8060–2	P 5/66	LM
D5271–6	Derby		P 6/64	LM	D7653–7	Beyer Peacock	8063–7	P 7/66	LM
D5277	Derby		P 7/64	LM	D7658/9	Beyer Peacock	8068/9	P 8/66	LM
D5278	Derby		P 6/64	LM	D7660	Derby		P13/66	LM
D5279–85	Derby		P 7/64	LM	D7661–4	Derby		P12/66	LM
D5286–93	Derby		P 9/64	LM	D7665/6	Derby		P13/66	LM
D5294–8	Derby		P10/64	LM	D7667/8	Derby		P 1/67	LM
D5299	Derby		P11/65	LM	D7669	Derby		P 3/67	LM
D7500	Derby		P10/64	LM	D7670	Derby		P 1/67	LM
D7501–7	Derby		P11/64	LM	D7671/2	Derby		P 2/67	LM
D7508–14	Derby		P12/64	LM	D7673/4	Derby		P 3/67	LM
D7515–8	Derby		P13/64	LM	D7675/6	Derby		P 4/67	LM
D7519	Derby		P 1/65	LM	D7677	Derby		P 5/67	LM
D7520	Derby		P13/64	LM					
D7521–7	Derby		P 1/65	LM					
D7528–33	Derby		P 2/65	LM					
D7534–8	Derby		P 3/65	LM					
D7540–3	Derby		P 4/65	LM					
D7544–8	Derby		P 5/65	LM					
D7549–51	Derby		P 6/65	LM					
D7552–6	Derby		P 7/65	LM					
D7557/8	Derby		P 8/65	LM					
D7559	Derby		P 9/65	LM					
D7560	Derby		P10/65	LM					
D7561	Derby		P11/65	LM					
D7562/3	Derby		P12/65	LM					
D7564	Derby		P13/65	LM					
D7565	Derby		P12/65	LM					
D7566/7	Derby		P 1/66	LM					
D7568	Derby		P10/63	LM					
D7569	Derby		P11/63	LM					
D7570	Derby		P10/63	LM					
D7571–4	Derby		P11/63	LM					
D7575–7	Derby		P12/63	LM					
D7578	Darlington		P12/63	LM					
D7579–81	Darlington		P13/63	LM					
D7582/3	Darlington		P 1/64	LM					
D7584/5	Darlington		P 2/64	LM					
D7586–8	Darlington		P 3/64	LM					
D7589	Darlington		P 4/64	LM					
D7590–2	Darlington		P 5/64	LM					
D7593/4	Darlington		P 6/64	LM					
D7595/6	Darlington		P 7/64	LM					
D7597	Darlington		P 9/64	LM					
D7598–603	Derby		2/66	E					
D7604–7	Derby		3/66	E					
D7608–10	Derby		4/66	E					
D7611/2	Derby		P 4/66	Sc					
D7613–6	Derby		P 5/66	Sc					
D7617	Derby		P 8/66	Sc					
D7618–23	Derby		P 9/66	Sc					
D7624/5	Beyer Peacock	8034/5	7/65	E					
D7629–31	Beyer Peacock	8039–41	9/65	E					
D7632–4	Beyer Peacock	8042–4	10/65	E					
D7635–40	Beyer Peacock	8045–50	11/65	E					
D7641/2	Beyer Peacock	8051/2	1/66	E					
D7643/4	Beyer Peacock	8053/4	2/66	E					
D7645/6	Beyer Peacock	8055/6	3/66	E					

TABLE 4
RENUMBERING OF CREWE, DERBY, DARLINGTON AND BEYER PEACOCK BUILT Bo-Bo DIESEL ELECTRICS OF CLASSES 24 AND 25

Original No.	Renumbering
D5000	24 005
D5001–4	24 001–4
D5005	withdrawn
D5006–27	24 006–27
D5028	withdrawn
D5029–42	24 029–42
D5043	withdrawn
D5044–50	24 044–50
D5051	withdrawn
D5052–66	24 052–66
D5067/8	withdrawn
D5069–87	24 069–87
D5088	withdrawn
D5089–92	24 089–92
D5093	withdrawn
D5094–113	24 094–113
D5114	withdrawn
D5115–21	24 115–21
D5122	withdrawn
D5123–30	24 123–30
D5131	withdrawn
D5132–7	24 132–7
D5138/9	withdrawn
D5140–8	24 140–8
D5149	withdrawn
D5150	24 150
D5151–277	25 001–127
D5278	withdrawn
D5279–99	25 129–49
D7500–604	25 150–254
D7605	withdrawn
D7606–77	25 256–327

Locomotives shown as withdrawn were not allocated new numbers.

CHAPTER 4
THE BRITISH RAIL DERBY TYPE 4—CLASSES 44, 45 AND 46

The choice of names to commemorate British peaks and mountains was, it has been opined, very appropriate for these very bulky and heavy locomotives. With a weight of 138 tons, they earned for BR many brickbats, especially as another BR workshop was building diesel-hydraulics of almost the same power, but only weighing 78 tons. The design was originally proposed as a Co-Co but, due to trying to follow conventional construction principles, it proved impossible to keep within a 20 tons maximum axle-loading imposed by the BR Civil Engineer, who also preferred a leading/guiding axle for his track's sake.

There was, unfortunately, on hand an existing design of 1Co bogie, the obsolete legacy of the Bulleid Ashford and Brighton-built 1Co-Co1 1750/2000bhp locomotives 10201-3, which was also forced onto English Electric for its 2000bhp class 40 locomotives for BR. The idea of a 1Co bogie was to offer relief of rail stresses, but the spacing of the axles on the BR locomotives, especially axles four and five of the 1Co-Co1 layout—that is, the last and first axle of each bogie—due to the distance between the bogies,

gave critical loadings to these axles. The layout was thus no advantage in these locomotives.

The superstructure of this Derby 2300/2500bhp design is to some extent similar to the class 24/25 Bo-Bo, but there are some important differences, due mainly to bogie/body support, and buffing requirements. Main body components are two continuous 10in × 3½in side channel members which curve at the ends, joining in the centre. A box section is provided down the centre, which also acts as an air duct for traction motor ventilation; cross-members join the whole together. Segmental pivot bearings carried on the cross-members are provided at the bogie positions. A drainage tray is provided below the engine room to protect traction undergear from oil/water spillage and runs full length between the cab bulkheads. The body side-frames are of bridge-girder type with diagonal bracing welded to the underframe. At cant-rail level, cross-members tie the sides together. The body is clad with steel sheet. Apertures for ventilation grilles in the upper body-sides are covered by long cover units to mask the irregular grilles, and to give an integrated design and improve appearance. No bodyside doors or windows are fitted other than in the cabs.

The roof follows the design of classes 24/25, but is of steel rather than aluminium. Over the engine room it is detachable as a complete section, access doors being provided for maintenance purposes. During refurbishing in the mid-1960s, split roofs were fitted in some cases to simplify stripping-down during cylinder head

The first Derby type 4, class 44 2300bhp 1Co-Co1 diesel-electric D1 *Scafell Pike*, being finished off in the paint shop at Derby works on Sunday, 19 April 1959. The originally striking green livery, with its low broad band and bodyside grilles picked out in light grey, presented a much more pleasing effect than the all over blue, and yellow nose ends now their lot today.　　　　　　　　　　　*(Brian Webb)*

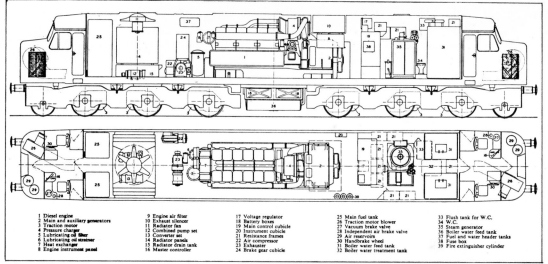

1 Diesel engine	9 Engine air filter	17 Voltage regulator	33 Flush tank for W.C.
2 Main and auxiliary generators	10 Exhaust silencer	18 Battery boxes	34 W.C.
3 Traction motor	11 Radiator fan	19 Main control cubicle	35 Steam generator
4 Pressure charger	12 Combined pump set	20 Instrument cubicle	36 Boiler water feed tank
5 Lubricating oil filter	13 Converter set	21 Resistance frames	37 Fuel and water header tanks
6 Lubricating oil strainer	14 Radiator panels	22 Air compressor	38 Fuse box
7 Heat exchanger	15 Radiator drain tank	23 Exhauster	39 Fire extinguisher cylinder
8 Engine instrument panel	16 Master controller	24 Brake gear cubicle	25 Main fuel tank
		26 Traction motor blower	
		27 Vacuum brake valve	
		28 Independent air brake valve	
		29 Air reservoirs	
		30 Handbrake wheel	
		31 Boiler water feed tank	
		32 Boiler water treatment tank	

Equipment layout diagram of class 44 2300bhp
locomotive. Class 45 was almost identical.
(Collection of B. Webb)

maintenance and removal of turbo-chargers.
The eth-fitted 45/1 were those mainly so modified.

The roof-mounted top filling point and hatch
for the train heating boiler water tank has been
eliminated due to the disappearance of water
cranes at stations. The associated alloy hatch was
often lost at speed or by hitting overline structures; this is now plated over, conforming to the
roof shape. At the same time, the bodyside inset
footsteps have been plated over.

The cabs of nose type are of steel construction,
housing auxiliary equipment and originally gangway connections. The cab interior followed
standard BR requirements, and had a raised floor
to improve visibility over the nose.

The bogies have a leading non-motored guiding axle and three powered axles. Compared to
the original Ashford bogie of locomotives 10201–
3, new springing was provided to deal with
additional weight, and manganese liners added to
the axlebox guides. A pony truck is used for the
guiding axle, being located inside the bogie frame
and controlled by side springs and loaded
spherical seated springs. Two pairs of links with
spherical bearings fixed to the bogie buffer beam
give the truck required movement. A Tecalemit
axle-driven pump lubricates the truck linkage
and pivot. Bogie loading is carried on a segmental oil-bath bearing ring, and takes the locomotive superstructure on a turntable rather than
pivot and bolster. The bogie frame is of steel
plate constructed by riveting and welding. Laminated main, coil auxiliary and rubber springs are

fitted. Springing is directly applied to the driving
axleboxes. The axleboxes and their springing
have given little trouble, although the coil
auxiliary springs do break, but these are easily
changed. The roller bearing axleboxes give good
service, apart from some seizing of the cannon
boxes on the pony truck in early years. Both
Timken and SKF axleboxes are fitted in the
classes 44/45/46, the former being originally oil-
lubricated, but all are now lubricated by grease.
All boxes are interchangeable and may be mixed
on the same bogie, although used in correct pairs
on each axle.

As in the EE class 40 locomotives, the bogies
suffer from frame fractures at a number of points.
These mainly occur in the top of the side frame
to the rear of the first cross-member. Close
observation is kept on cracks until they extend to
three inches, at which point the locomotives have
to go to main works for welding. A serious loss of
availability can result, as the bogies are not prone
to go from one general repair to another without
fracturing. Although various methods have been
used to combat this, it was not until 45018
received in 1974 a pony truck with Flexicoil
pivots, instead of the old pivotless arrangement,
and operated since without trouble. In this
experiment the front end of each bogie was
rebuilt to take a pony truck swinging from a
central fixed pivot block behind the first cross-
member. The side swing is controlled by plunger
dampers and limit stops, and the ride by two
large coil springs acting vertically on the truck
'A' frame.

The standard truck is expensive and difficult to
maintain. The spring pad links and pans have a

high rate of wear, often losing securing nuts; the pins then work loose and the links thus freed drop down and become bent. Even so, the bogies ride well, rough riding at high speeds and mileages usually being due to flats on the tyres, worn or dry segmental bearings, or broken nose bolster support springs.

Bogie rotational stops and side control buffers were removed from classes 44, 45 and 46 after trials with D15 in 1971. It was found that passing round curves of less than five chains radius was causing these fitments to contribute to bogie frame fractures. Removal has permitted negotiation of three-and-a-half chain curves, this being the absolute limit for the 1Co bogie. The bogies will accept the traction motors of all three classes, giving a useful standardisation quality. However, on the eth locomotives the bogies were altered to take the required cabling and the steam heat pipes were removed. These bogies are thus restricted to class 45/1 unless reversion to the previous layout is undertaken.

Machinery layout provides for a central compartment housing engine/generator set, main control cubicle, voltage regulator, lubricating oil filter, an Oerlikon air compressor, an SLM vacuum-exhauster of type 30, brake cubicle, and in the roof fuel and water header tanks. The layout of these items is not good; those requiring renewal have to be manhandled into No 1 cab, negotiate the 9in difference in floor level into the cab, and to permit exit both the engine room and cab doors have to be taken off.

The vacuum-exhauster gives trouble, being located in the centre of the compartment, its removal taking 8–12 hours. In the class 44/45 units, the CP auxiliary motors give trouble due to their having only two brushes, thereby needing a higher starting current, resulting in brush and commutator wear. The Brush motors in class 46 have four brushes, and fare better. Traction motor blower failures, probably due to the dirty environment in the locomotive noses, suffer from commutator and armature wear. The rotary motor-convertor set which reduces the 220V from the battery to 110V for the control circuit gives little trouble; this has, of course, been removed from class 45/1, which uses its eth supply via a rectifier for control.

Originally the 96-cell 220V battery was easily exhausted because with the original electro-pnuematic starter contactor it was necessary to run the air compressor from the battery to obtain sufficient air pressure (40lb/sq in) to turn the engine over; at the same time it had to power the combined pump set which circulated the fuel, lubricating oil and cooling water through the engine, and provide the locomotive lighting! Repeated attempts at starting quickly flattened the battery, and subsequent recharging at high rates caused rapid battery deterioration and short life. The fitting of electro-magnetic starting has largely overcome this difficulty.

The radiator compartment has side-mounted radiators of Serck type, air being drawn over them by a two-speed CP-powered electric fan mounted in the roof. This compartment also houses the Sulzer combined pump set driven by a CP motor, and the main fuel tanks—one each side of the centre access corridor from the driving cab. At the other end is located the train-heating boiler—a Stone-Vapor unit, boiler water feed tanks and treatment tanks in the roof, and the toilet.

The main train-heating water tank and locomotive batteries are slung from the underframe. Considerable trouble was experienced with the water tanks due to fractures, repair work often requiring complete removal of the tanks for welding, not an easy task for the depot staff.

The nose units house Aerex-Hyperform traction motor blowers—one each end for its respec-

Class 44 Speed/tractive effort curves.

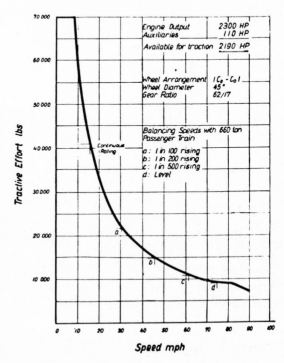

tive bogie, and air reservoirs. Brake equipment is by Metcalfe-Oerlikon, the locomotive being air-braked.

Locomotive D2 was selected for experimental work, including engine uprating to 2500bhp prior to the general availability of the rating as standard. It was also arranged for speeds over 90mph, and its gearing modified accordingly. High-speed tests with D2 on the Euston–Liverpool section included seven-coach trains of 230 tons which covered the 193 miles in 156½ minutes, at an average of 74mph, with a maximum of 105mph. With only three-coach trains 110mph was reached.

The trials in connection with electrification of the route were to establish, by using a track-recording coach, which portions of track required modification before high-speed electric haulage of passenger trains started. D2 was officially derated to its standard 2300bhp on 23 February 1963.

The next batch of locomotives was to be the class 45 numbered D11–147, which was subsequently reduced by ten to end at D137. They were very similar to the first ten units of class 44, but they were modified to give traction characteristics more suitable for mixed-traffic work and to take advantage of the 'B' version of the twin-bank engine of 2500bhp.

D1–10 had starting and continuous tractive effort ratings of 70,000lb and 41,000lb at 16·5mph respectively, but D11–137 had 55,000lb and 30,000lb at 25mph. A smaller traction motor, CP C172A1 was used, but the generator remained the same.

From the maintenance point of view the whole of the CP-equipped batches are very similar. The traction motors are easy for maintenance as their brush boxes are mounted on a ring which can be rotated around the commutator to permit attention via the bottom access hatch. During the 1960s hairline cracks appeared in many of the armature shafts; those found too bad by ultra-sonic testing had to be replaced, but in due course modified shafts cured the problem.

Insulation breakdown, armature binding failure and loose commutator bars (the latter due probably to locomotive over-speeding) cause problems. Flashovers are not uncommon and this proves difficult to remedy, as the usual cause, dirt, does not appear to be the culprit. Eastern Region class 45s seem to get most of their problems while in the hands of Western Region crews.

Pressure-charger failures in class 45 were caused by the breakage of the turbine blades after 8,000–12,000 miles' running. Tests revealed the culprit to be temperature variation between the root of the blade and the tip being much higher than planned. Modified wire-threaded blades were produced and fitted over an 18-month period, by which time 10 per cent of the locomotives had been affected.

The increase in engine output from 2300 to 2500bhp, with its resultant increased cylinder pressures, caused deterioration of the cylinder heads and liner joints, allowing the gases to escape. A strengthened head was put on which eliminated gas blow-by.

The final class 45 taken into stock was Crewe-built D57 in July 1963. This locomotive had its engine uprated to 2750bhp at 800rpm and spent some two-and-a-half years undergoing tests at Derby and on the line before entering normal duties. D57 was also provided with engine pressure-cooling, the first BR locomotive to be so equipped. This was introduced to improve performance, reduce cavitation corrosion and the actual size of the cooling system. These are all aspects which increase in importance as locomotives increase in size and power. It was thus possible to obviate increases in auxiliaries such as radiator size and capacity. In common with its standard brethren, D57 had radiator coolant drain tanks, this requiring the cooling system to be pressurized by air supplied at 20lb/sq in through a pressure reducing non-return valve from the locomotives air brake system. At maximum engine rpm, the pressure at the pump inlet was 18lb/sq in and 38lb/sq in respectively.

A number of serious bogie fires which in traffic were caused by the locomotives braking before their trains braked, the weight and momentum of the trains pushing the locomotives along with brakes applied. The resulting friction sparks then ignited oil and dirt deposits. Modifications to the braking system overcame this problem.

The introduction of electric train heating saw the class 45 locomotives slectively fitted with Brush type BL 100-30 Mk II heating generators. The 50 locomotives chosen form class 45/1, 45 101–50. The eth control cabinet is fitted in place of the boiler, the redundant water tanks being replaced by small cast-iron ballast weights, firebottles and repositioning of toilet water tank.

The next order for 1Co-Co1 locomotives involved a change in electric traction equipment supplier. Owing to existing large orders placed at CP for generators and traction motors for classes

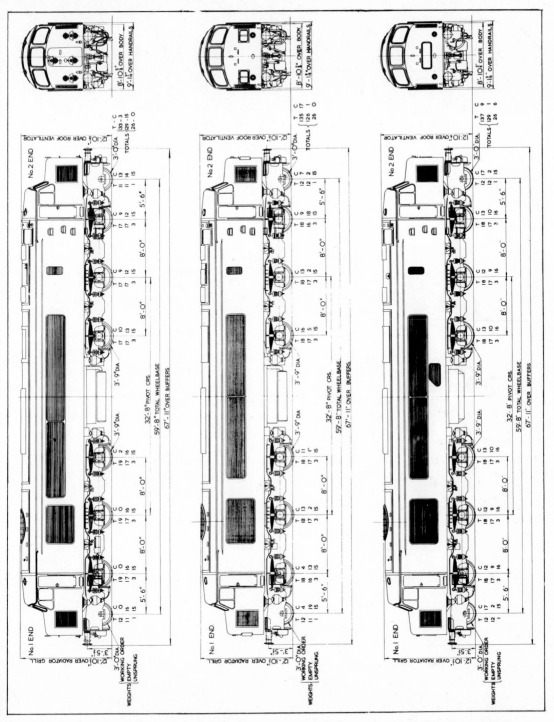

Comparative side and end elevations of the BR Derby type 4. *Left :* Class 44 2300bhp Sulzer–Crompton Parkinson equipped version, with nose corridor connections and lights and discs for headcode requirements. *Centre :* Class 45 2500bhp Sulzer–Crompton Parkinson equipped locomotive without nose corridor connections, and with split type four-digit indicator boxes. Some class 45 had corridor connections and others had none, but all had either split or centrally placed indicator boxes. *Right :* Class 46 2500bhp Sulzer–Brush equipped locomotive. All these were built with centre-mounted four-digit indicators.

(British Railways)

Classes 44 and 45, 44 004 and D39, sit in the Corby steelworks sidings of Stewarts & Lloyds Ltd awaiting their next duties in August 1974.   *(Fred Kerr)*

26, 33 and 45, coupled with BR's increasingly demanding delivery dates, the Chelmsford works of CP, and their Norwich subcontractor Laurence, Scott and Electromotors Ltd, could not offer the delivery BR required, so a change was made. The new order was for 76 locomotives to be numbered D138–99/D1500–13, but subsequently reduced by 20 sets of equipment so that Brush could use them in a Co-Co diesel-electric of much reduced weight for BR. They became class 46, renumbered 46001–56, and delivered from Derby works to LMR and NER.

These locomotives are of 2500bhp and have the Brush type TG160-60 main generator, continuously rated at 2100A, 765V, 1650kW. The overhung auxiliary generator is Brush type TG69-28, rated at 432A, 110V, 47·5kW at 468/ 1080rpm. Six Brush axle-hung and nose suspended, force-ventilated traction motors of type TM73-68 Mk III are fitted. The single-reduction gear ratio is 62:19.

Auxiliaries include a pair of Brush traction-motor blower motors of type TAM28-16 Mk I running at 2440rpm and putting out 110V, 97A to drive two Sturtevant blowers. Air comes from a Davies & Metcalfe-Oerlikon compressor giving 110V, 80A at 2900rpm. The fitting of automatic air brake in addition to retaining locomotive air and train vacuum braking, resulted in uprating the compressor motor to 136A at 3690rpm. The SLM VL30 vacuum exhauster has a Brush type TAM28-27 motor producing 110A, 80A at 1000rpm.

The combined Sulzer service pump set—dealing as usual with cooling water circulation, lubricating oil priming pump and fuel transfer, was powered by a Brush TAM28-16 Mk II motor,

running at 2440rpm, 110V, 105A. Engine cooling radiators are by Serck-Behr, as on classes 44 and 45, but the roof-mounted fan in class 46 has hydrostatic drive instead of electric. A Spanner Mk III steam generator provides train heating. Corridor gangways are not provided in class 46, all being built with centrally located one-piece four-digit indicator boxes in their nose units.

The twin-bank engine suffered stress failures similar to those experienced with class 47 with the 2750bhp engine, but not so severely. It was, however, necessary to do modifications, these being dealt with in Chapter 6. Failures do still occur with both the 'A' and 'B' versions of the 12LDA28 engine, including crankcase A-frame fractures adjacent to fractures previously repaired by welding—a trend reported to be following a 36-month cycle in mid-1976. Peculiarly, the crankcase sill plates and fuel pump trays fracture mainly on locomotives with eth equipment. The Sulzer twin-bank engine is easier for working on than the Vee type engine of EE manufacture. Fitters can stand half-way up the engine to work comfortably on the cylinder heads, valve gear, exhaust pipes, etc. This is particularly helpful as the Sulzer engine demands more top maintenance than the EE engine.

Exhaust silencers have been altered to improve durability and reduce time spent on maintenance, this chiefly involving the replacement of flexible metal bellows prone to splitting due to too rigid mountings, by short detachable tail pieces which slide into the silencer opening, being packed with asbestos rope to exclude fumes. This itself has failed, and in 45119 the silencer has been removed. Class 46 suffer less from split bellows as their silencers are flexibly mounted. Some problems with blocked and inefficiently cleaned nose side filters caused revision of these so that cleaning equipment could handle them; two smaller filter units replacing one large one.

Above: No 45 046, with a damaged indicator box, runs into Sunderland with the 17.05 Brian Mills depot–Sheffield parcels train on 7 June 1976. *(Ian S. Carr)*

Below: A down coal train leaving Baronswood tunnel behind class 45 45 021 on 27 May 1975. *(Brian Webb)*

The nose units in the three variants differ considerably, class 44 having corridor connections and end doors, with train description discs and lights. Class 45 in earlier examples had corridor connections and doors but with the split or wing type train indicator boxes, two digits per box. As the corridor connections were hardly ever used, they were discontinued. Some locomotives received wing boxes but no doors, in others the two boxes were arranged side by side in the centre of the nose front; finally the single four-digit box was fitted. Nose replacement has also confused the situation. The elimination of the indicator boxes and fitting of twin headlights commenecd with D125 (45071), ex Derby works in early 1976 following some 18 months there after running into another train at Bridgwater in October 1974. Cab windscreens, originally double-glazed and demister wired, have been progressively replaced by Triplex gold-film laminated screens which demist by a current passing through the gold film.

Construction of class 44 locomotives D1–D10 commenced at Derby in the late summer of 1958, frames being laid down for two locomotives, but it was not until 21 April 1959 that D1 was sent down to St Pancras for official inspection. Although built with its nameplates, D1 was ceremonially named *Scafell Pike* at Carlisle on 14 July 1959, and from this theme came the class title as the 'Peak' class. During August 1959, D1 was allocated to Camden depot, but on loan to Derby, where it was on Midland line duties from

A now vanished sight, class 45 D100 *Sherwood Forester* taking water through the roof top hatch for train-heating boiler supply at York station on 5 May 1962. D100 was the first class 45 to be named.
(Brian Webb)

October. All ten locomotives were allocated to Camden, but remained at Derby, being very rarely seen on West Coast main line duties until early 1960 when they were scattered to Edge Hill, Longsight, Crewe North and Carlisle (Upperby) depots, in addition to Camden, for crew training.

Upon delivery of the class 45 2500bhp locomotives the class 44s were considered 'odd men

The first class 46 was D138. Here as 138 and with a broken cab window it is seen on the WR at Teignmouth with the 09.25 Derby–Penzance on 14 August 1971. It is in green livery with all-yellow nose.
(Norman E. Preedy)

out', and in due course all went to Toton for a life mostly spent on heavy freight duties, a task for which they were especially suited. Later the class was modified in its tractive effort to bring it into line with class 45. All class 44 locomotives had their steam heating generators taken out, but withdrawal did not start until July 1976, during which year their nameplates were removed. Withdrawn examples have been stripped at Derby for spares to keep classes 45 and 46 in traffic.

Like the class 44, the class 45 locomotives were to spend most time on Midland line work. This seemed strange when the EE 2000bhp locomotives of class 40, which were lower in power, were given the more arduous duties on the West Coast main line. Both Crewe and Derby works turned out class 45 during 1960–62, the majority

coming from Crewe due to transfer of some batches from Derby—hence locomotives built in batches out of numerical order. Although Derby and Crewe North received new 45s, they all finished-up on the Midland line where, in addition to Derby, they were based at Cricklewood and Toton depots.

With a view to their use on through St Pancras–Glasgow services, D11 and D14 were lent to the NER at Leeds (Neville Hill) for the training of its own and Holbeck crews. This was done on the Settle & Carlisle line and to Newcastle upon Tyne in early 1960. D13 was loaned to Sheffield Darnall in early 1961 and worked dynamometer car trains of up to 14 coaches on the Doncaster–New England run, for testing and high-speed braking purposes.

To enable the NER to participate in Midland line diesel working of Anglo-Scottish trains, D11–16 were moved to Holbeck in March 1961, to be followed by others. In mid-1961, the 'Thames-Clyde' and 'Waverley' expresses fell to class 45 haulage, and from July all regular Leeds–Glasgow trains were so worked.

A class 46 in the latest form, with twin headlights in place of the indicator box, in this case 46 048 bending its train through the platforms of Monkwearmouth station (now Monkwearmouth Station Museum) with the 01.15 King's Cross–Newcastle (via the coast) on 20 April 1977.   *(Ian S. Carr)*

Pending introduction on Bristol–Birmingham–Newcastle upon Tyne services, D93 was lent to the WR in spring 1961 and was on Bristol–Gloucester services for crew training. By June the class was regularly visiting Bristol. Later in 1961 a batch of 45s was transferred to Bristol. Since that time the class has continued on similar duties, but still the Midland line is their scene. In 1977 they were at Cricklewood, Toton, Holbeck and Tinsley.

The class 46 derivative started to come into traffic in late 1961, going to Derby and Gateshead depots. The LMR locomotives, D138–65, were put on work similar to that of the 45s, but D154 was lent to the ER at Finsbury Park in February 1962 for crew training, doing some work on King's Cross–Hull trains during March and April. Gateshead received D166–93, which were put to work on Newcastle–Liverpool trains and on East Coast main line duties. Transfers took them to Holbeck, while others were loaned to Edge Hill on the LMR and to the Scottish Region at Haymarket. Later on, Gateshead locomotives were loaned to the WR at Bristol in 1971. From 1971 all the LMR locomotives went to the WR at Bristol, to be followed in 1972 by some of the ER locomotives which went to Plymouth Laira, while others went to Bristol.

When the production of class 47 at the Loughborough works of Brush Traction was nearing the end, a four-year contract was negotiated with

A rare view of the Sulzer refurbishing work in progress in the works of Brush Traction at Loughborough. At the front, left to right, are class 46s 168, 182 and 176, and an unidentifiable class 45. In the background are further locomotives, together with five class 47 under construction.   *(Brush Electrical Machines)*

BR to provide continuation of work. This provided for the overhaul and refurbishing of Sulzer-engined BR locomotives of 1160–2500bhp at Loughborough, and was a unique arrangement so far as this country was concerned, although it is common practice in many overseas countries which do not have such elaborate railway-owned workshops. Class 46 D154 was the first locomotive to be dealt with, in early 1965.

Apart from the ten class 44 locomotives bearing the names of British peaks from their construction, no more names were given until 1961 when D100 became *Sherwood Forester*, initiating a seven-year programme of naming for a total of 25 locomotives of class 45 and one of class 46. The names were those used on the ex-LMSR 'Royal Scot' and 'Patriot' class steam locomotives, or of similar origin.

The Derby Type 4 has certainly served BR well, and at the end of 1977, except for the inroads made into the class 44 variant, only two

others have been withdrawn for scrapping. 45067 was withdrawn following a rear-end collision with a derailed coal train at near Ilkeston, on 8 July 1977, while working a Glasgow–Nottingham express. It was withdrawn on 31 July. 46005 was withdrawn on 4 December. The class 45 is probably the best of the Sulzer type 4s on BR.

TABLE 5
NAMED CLASS 45 AND 46 LOCOMOTIVES
OF BRITISH RAILWAYS

Number	Name	Date
D1	Scafell Pike	9/59
D2	Helvellyn	10/59
D3	Skiddaw	10/59
D4	Great Gable	10/59
D5	Cross Fell	11/59
D6	Whernside	12/59
D7	Ingleborough	12/59
D8	Penyghent	12/59
D9	Snowdon	12/59
D10	Tryfan	2/60
D49	The Manchester Regiment	10/65
D50	King's Shropshire Light Infantry	5/65
D52	The Lancashire Fusilier	10/67
D53	Royal Tank Regiment	9/64
D54	The Royal Pioneer Corps	11/63
D55	Royal Signals	6/65

Number	Name	Date
D56	The Bedfordshire and Hertfordshire	
	Regiment (TA)	12/62
D58	The King's Own Royal Border Regiment	5/63
D59	The Royal Warwickshire Fusilier	5/64
D60	Lytham St Annes	5/64
D61	Royal Army Ordnance Corps	9/65
D62	Fifth Royal Inniskilling Dragoon Guards	1/64
D63	Royal Inniskilling Fusilier	10/65
D64	Coldstream Guardsman	4/65
D65	Grenadier Guardsman	5/64
D67	The Royal Artilleryman	10/65
D68	Royal Fusilier	1/67
D70	The Royal Marines	12/64
D71	The Staffordshire Regiment (Prince of	
	Wales' Own)	5/66
D77	Royal Irish Fusilier	9/65
D84	Royal Corps of Transport	6/66
D89	Honourable Artillery Company	6/65
D98	Royal Engineer	12/66
D99	Third Carabinier	12/65
D100	Sherwood Forester	9/61
D137	The Cheshire Regiment	6/66
D163	Leicestershire and Derbyshire Yeomanry	4/62

Note: D1–D10 were built with nameplates, so dates quoted
are the dates into traffic.

TABLE 7
BUILDING WORKS AND DATES INTO RUNNING STOCK OF CLASSES 44, 45 AND 46 1Co-Co1 DIESEL ELECTRIC LOCOMOTIVES

Number	Builder	Date	Region
D1	Derby	P 9/59	LM
D2–4	Derby	P10/59	LM
D5	Derby	P11/59	LM
D6/7	Derby	P12/59	LM
D8/9	Derby	P13/59	LM
D10	Derby	P 2/60	LM
D11	Derby	P10/60	LM
D12/3	Derby	P11/60	LM
D14	Derby	P12/60	LM
D15–9	Derby	P13/60	LM
D20	Derby	P 2/61	LM
D21	Derby	P 3/61	LM
D22–6	Derby	P 4/61	LM
D27–30	Derby	P 5/61	LM
D31/2	Derby	P 6/61	LM
D33–8	Derby	P 7/61	LM
D39–41	Derby	P 8/61	LM
D42–5	Derby	P 9/61	LM
D46–9	Derby	P10/61	LM
D50–2	Crewe	P 6/62	LM
D53	Crewe	P 7/62	LM

TABLE 6
MAIN VARIATIONS IN CLASSES 44, 45 AND 46 1Co-Co1 DIESEL ELECTRICS, BASED ON BRITISH RAIL DIAGRAM BOOK MT25 OF 1974

Number series	44 001–10	45 001–77	45 001–77	45 101–50	46 001–56	46 001–56
Former number series	D1–D10	D11–D137	D11–D137	D11–D137	D138–D193	D138–D193
Class	44	45/0	45/0	45/1	46	46
Diagram number	44 aV	45 aV	45 bX	45 1aX	46 aX	46 bX
Weight in working order	133ton 3cwt	134ton 12cwt	135ton 7cwt	132ton 16cwt	138ton 6cwt	138ton 4cwt
Fuel capacity, gal.	790	790	790	790	790	790
Boiler water capacity, gal.	—	1040	1040	—	1040	1040
Generator type	CP CG426A1	CP CG426A1	CP CG426A1	CP CG426A1	BT TG160-60	BT TG160-60
Traction motor type	CP C171B1	CP C172A1	CP C172A1	CP C172A1	BT TM73-68 Mk III	BT TM73-68 Mk III
Rail hp	1800	2000	2000	2000	1962	1962
Maximum tractive effort, lb	70,000 later 50,000	55,000	55,000	55,000	55,000	55,000
Continuous tractive effort, lb/mph	41,000 later 29,100/23·2	30,000/25	30,000/25	30,000/25	31,600/23·3	31,600/23·3
Train heating { Boiler type	—	Vapor OK4625	Vapor OK4625	—	Vapor OK4625	Spanner Mk III
Train heating { eth	—	—	—	BL100-30	—	—
Braking { Locomotive	A	A	A	SA AA	SA AA	SA AA
Braking { Train	V	V	V	AA ACV	AA ACV	AA ACV

For full details of individual locomotive renumbering see Table No. 8.

Number	Builder	Date	Region
D54	Crewe	P 8/62	LM
D55	Crewe	P10/62	LM
D56	Crewe	P12/62	LM
D57	Crewe	P 7/63	LM
D58–60	Crewe	P 2/62	LM
D61/2	Crewe	P 3/62	LM
D63–6	Crewe	P 4/62	LM
D67	Crewe	P 5/62	LM
D68	Crewe	P10/60	LM
D69	Crewe	P11/60	LM
D70–3	Crewe	P12/60	LM
D74	Crewe	P13/60	LM
D75/6	Crewe	P12/60	LM
D77–84	Crewe	P13/60	LM
D85	Crewe	P 2/61	LM
D86	Crewe	P 3/61	LM
D87	Crewe	P 2/61	LM
D88–92	Crewe	P 3/61	LM
D93–7	Crewe	P 4/61	LM
D98–102	Crewe	P 5/61	LM
D103–6	Crewe	P 6/61	LM
D107	Crewe	P 7/61	LM
D108	Crewe	P 8/61	LM
D109	Crewe	P 7/61	LM
D110–2	Crewe	P 8/61	LM
D113–7	Crewe	P 9/61	LM
D118–21	Crewe	P10/61	LM
D122–5	Crewe	P11/61	LM
D126–9	Crewe	P12/61	LM
D130–7	Crewe	P13/61	LM
D138/9	Derby	P11/61	LM
D140/1	Derby	P12/61	LM
D142	Derby	P13/61	LM
D143	Derby	P12/61	LM
D144–50	Derby	P13/61	LM
D151	Derby	P 1/62	LM
D152	Derby	P 2/62	LM
D153	Derby	P 1/62	LM
D154–6	Derby	P 2/62	LM
D157–9	Derby	P 3/62	LM
D160–4	Derby	P 4/62	LM
D165	Derby	P 5/62	LM
D166–8	Derby	5/62	NE
D169/70	Derby	6/62	NE
D171–4	Derby	7/62	NE
D175–7	Derby	8/62	NE
D178–82	Derby	9/62	NE
D183–5	Derby	10/62	NE
D186/7	Derby	11/62	NE
D188	Derby	12/62	NE
D189–93	Derby	1/63	NE

TABLE 8
RENUMBERING OF DERBY AND CREWE BUILT
1Co-Co1 DIESEL ELECTRICS OF
CLASSES 44, 45 AND 46

Original No.	Renumbering	Original No.	Renumbering
D1–10	44 001–10	D78	45 054
D11	45 112	D79	45 005
D12	45 011	D80	45 110
D13	45 001	D81	45 115
D14	45 015	D82/3	45 141/2
D15	45 018	D84	45 055
D16	45 016	D85	45 109
D17	45 024	D86	45 105
D18	45 121	D87	45 127
D19	45 025	D88	45 136
D20	45 013	D89	45 006
D21	45 026	D90	45 008
D22	45 132	D91	45 056
D23	45 017	D92	45 138
D24	45 027	D93	45 057
D25	45 021	D94	45 114
D26	45 020	D95	45 150
D27	45 028	D96	45 101
D28	45 124	D97/8	45 058/9
D29	45 002	D99	45 135
D30/1	45 029/30	D100/1	45 060/1
D32	45 126	D102	45 140
D33	45 019	D103–5	45 062–4
D34	45 119	D106	45 106
D35	45 117	D107	45 120
D36	45 031	D108	45 012
D37	45 009	D109	45 139
D38/9	45 032/3	D110	45 065
D40	45 133	D111	45 129
D41	45 147	D112	45 010
D42	45 034	D113	45 128
D43	45 107	D114/5	45 066/7
D44–6	45 035–7	D116	45 103
D47	45 116	D117	45 130
D48–50	45 038–40	D118	45 068
D51	45 102	D119	45 007
D52	45 123	D120	45 108
D53	45 041	D121/2	45 069/70
D54	45 023	D123	45 125
D55	45 144	D124	45 131
D56	45 137	D125	45 071
D57/8	45 042/3	D126	45 134
D59	45 104	D127	45 072
D60	45 022	D128	45 145
D61	45 112	D129	45 073
D62	45 143	D130	45 148
D63/4	45 044/5	D131/2	45 074/5
D65	45 111	D133	45 003
D66	45 146	D134	45 076
D67	45 118	D135	45 149
D68–72	45 046–50	D136	45 077
D73	45 110	D137	45 014
D74–6	45 051–3	D138–93	46 001–56
D77	45 004		

CHAPTER 5

THE BIRMINGHAM SULZERS—CLASSES 26, 27 AND 33

The Birmingham Sulzers originated from a 1955 order for 20 Bo-Bo diesel-electrics under the pilot scheme of the BR modernisation programme. The design took advantage of the tripartite working association of BRCW/Sulzer/CP established for export work. This design of locomotive had much in common with the Derby type 2, both types using the same 1160bhp engine. At the time this was the nearest point to standardisation achieved in two different locomotive makes.

The mechanical design incorporates a welded steel underframe of two main double-channel longitudinals, tied by two main transoms at the bogie positions and two at the engine. Cooling ducts for the traction motors are welded to the longitudinals; buffing and drawgear pass through the fabricated headstocks into the dragbox, itself

Class 26 1160bhp D5301 and class 27 1250bhp D5347 stand at Edinburgh Haymarket depot in September 1971, illustrating the front end variations of these BRCW built locomotives. *(Fred Kerr)*

a fabricated structure. The superstructure is built up from 'I' section vertical and diagonal steel members forming a lattice-girder for support of underframe and equipment, in fact similar to the arrangement used in classes 24 and 25.

Above cant-rail level on both sides are louvres for the air filters of Vokes oil-wetted type. These filters handle all air admitted for engine cooling and ventilation, plus air for generator group and traction motor blowers. Similar filters are provided on the train-heating boiler compartment. Bodyside radiators are fitted for cooling the engine water and lubricating oil, air being drawn through by a roof-mounted fan which is electrically driven and thermostatically controlled.

The roof covering is of translucent glass-fibre mouldings, and is completely removable for maintenance access. The two driving cabs have moulded glass-fibre roof canopies, but the cabs themselves are of aluminium sheeting. All locomotives of class 26, D5300–46, had the gangway

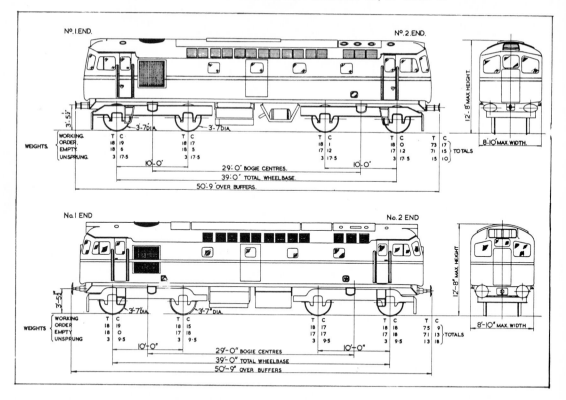

Diagram of BRCW class 27/1 (top) and 27/1bX (bottom).

provision for inter-locomotive access, but this has now been sealed up. Cab layout is in accord with BR practice.

The bogies are equalising-beam type with swing bolsters. The main members are of welded hollow-box formation made from mild steel plate, with dropped ends. The bolster is carried on four suspension links and sprung at both sides with triple eliptical springs; rubber stops are fitted to restrict transverse movement. The spring planks are of cast steel, each supported on two links from the cross-bars, and are tied together by rolled-steel angles. Four nests of helical springs carry the bogie frame through spring links onto high-level equalising beams. Bogie centre pivots are made of cast steel and are of deep socket flat bottom type with 20in diameter bearing seats. Manganese-steel liners take up traction and braking forces, the loading being taken by hard bronze liners between top and bottom pivot bearing faces. Axleboxes of SKF type with roller bearings are fitted; they have manganese-steel liners in the horn guides. Davies & Metcalfe-Oerlikon braking equipment is used, air for loco-

motive, vacuum for the train. An anti-slip brake is also provided.

The engine fitted is the Sulzer 6LDA28 of 1160bhp. This is coupled to a CP main generator which is a ten-pole single-bearing machine with separate and self-excitation, decompounding and starting windings. Its rating is 757kW, 1720A, at 750rpm. Both main and auxiliary generators are on a common cast-steel rotor with the 57kW

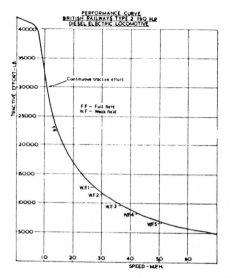

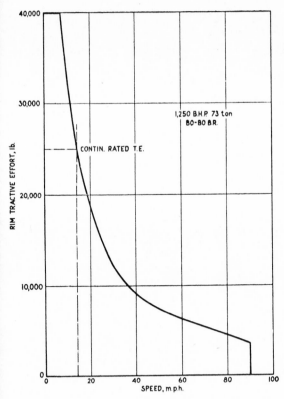

440V, and one-hour rating of 222hp, 470A, 400V. The gearing is single-reduction. The motors are nose-suspended on Metalastik rubber units. Traction motor blowing comes from an Aerex-Hypaform unit for each bogie. These are two-speed, CP-powered units running at 2150/2840rpm and of 14·2hp, housed in the engine compartment.

A Stone-Vapor steam-heating generator is carried, and the 100-gallon oil fuel tank for this is in the same compartment. The main fuel and water tanks are slung from the locomotive underframe, but roof-mounted fuel service tank and water-header tanks are carried inside the engine compartment. Locomotive control equipment is by Allen West Ltd.

The most interesting derivative of the Birmingham Sulzer was the type 3 1550bhp variant designed to meet Southern Region requirements. As class 33, this design remains BR's most powerful diesel-electric locomotive on four axles, and

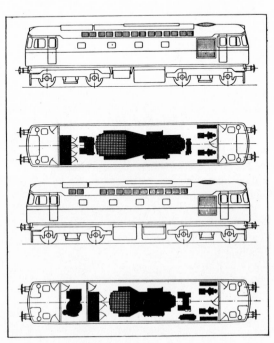

Diagrams showing the relative layout of power and auxiliary equipment of the BRCW built type 3 (class 33) top, and type 2 (classes 26 and 27) lower. Elimination of the steam train-heating equipment fitted in the class 26/27 permitted the installation of a larger engine and resulted in class 33 for the SR, the only Bo-Bo diesel-electric on BR to fall within the old type 3 classification   (Collection of B. Webb)

Speed/tractive effort curves: above, class 27; left lower, class 26; below, class 33.

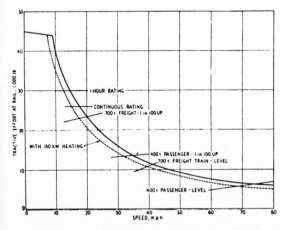

auxiliary unit built into the main machine. A Polling sector type voltage regulator maintains a constant tension of 110V throughout the engine speed range.

Four CP series-wound force-ventilated traction motors are fitted which, apart from the gear-ratio, are similar to those of classes 33, 44 and 45. They have a continuous rating of 224hp, 430A,

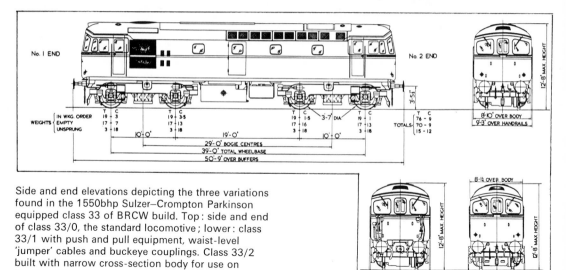

Side and end elevations depicting the three variations found in the 1550bhp Sulzer–Crompton Parkinson equipped class 33 of BRCW build. Top: side and end of class 33/0, the standard locomotive; lower: class 33/1 with push and pull equipment, waist-level 'jumper' cables and buckeye couplings. Class 33/2 built with narrow cross-section body for use on Hastings line.   *(British Railways)*

was the result of careful consideration of the individual needs of this region. Meeting these so well, almost 20 years after their appearance they remain the SR's only permanently allocated line service diesel-electric.

The elimination of steam-heating was an ideal solution of the problems which this apparatus caused to diesel locomotive availability, for many hundreds of BR diesels have failed due to steam-

Below: In ex-works condition, class 33/1 33 105, fitted for push and pull working, stands at Eastleigh depot in December 1975; behind it is a class 33/2 with narrower body.   *(Fred Kerr)*

heating malfunctions when their diagrammed duty demanded an operable one. The class 33 was therefore evolved by using the BRCW type 2 (class 26) mechanical portion, minus its steam generator, and fitting instead a larger diesel engine.

Electric train heating was chosen for the SR because passenger traffic was heavier in summer when heating was not required, while in winter the fact that the locomotives would be used mostly on freight did not make provision of even only a few locomotives with steam-heating economical. Moreover, the eth generator was arranged so that its output was available for traction when not used for heating, so no spare equipment had to be carried. The result was a Bo-Bo type 3, rather than a more costly Co-Co, which was also highly standardised. The mechanical portion was the same as the class 26, but the interior was more roomy, only one compartment being required between the cab bulkheads.

A total of 98 were built by BRCW and numbered D6500–97, having the 'Southern Electric' two-digit indicator fitted in the cab-front centre-window space; no gangway connections were fitted. The final 12 locomotives were built to a reduced width for use on the Hastings line with its restricted loading gauge.

The engine is the Sulzer 8LDA28 with an output of 1550bhp, being turbo-charged by a de Haviland-Sulzer unit mounted on top of the generator. Cooling is by a Serck-Behr system incorporating a hydrostatically-driven roof-mounted cooling fan, which is thermostatically controlled. Bodyside mounted oil and water-cooling radiators are fitted. The main fuel tank and pull-out battery boxes are hung from the underframe. Air intakes above cant rail admit filtered air to the engine compartment.

The CP generator group comprises three machines arranged integrally: a main generator, auxiliary generator and train-heating generator. The main machine is a ten-pole, self-ventilated unit with separately excited, decompounding and starting windings. It is rated at 1012kW, 575V, 1760A, at 750rpm. The auxiliary generator is an eight-pole unit continuously rated at 57kW, 110V, 518A, at 450rpm, the voltage being maintained at 110 at all engine speeds by an automatic voltage regulator.

Electric train heating is provided by a generator on the same shaft as the main and auxiliary machines. It is a separately excited machine rated at 235kW, 750V, 313A, 550rpm continuously.

When in use for heating, the generator requires engine idling speed to be raised from 350 to 550rpm to give sufficient output. It is compatible with BR two-pole, Continental and some SR rolling stock. Safety devices to prevent wrong usage are fitted with the two-pole system; if any jumper connection through the train is disconnected while the eth is in use, the feed to the heating contactors on the locomotive is automatically disconnected. When two or more locomotives are coupled in multiple, only the one coupled to the train provides the heating. A safety precaution prevents the jumpers of the other locomotive(s) from interconnecting, to prevent paralleling of the eth generators.

Each of the four CP traction motors has a continuous rating of 305hp, 440A, 580V. They are series-wound, force-ventilated machines, similar to those in BR classes 26, 44 and 45. They are axle-hung with flexible mountings in their nose-suspension. Single-reduction gears by Wiseman, with a ratio of 62:17, are fitted. Traction motor blowers are by CP, being in the engine room, one for each pair of motors. Locomotive air braking comes from a motor-driven Metcalfe-Oerlikon compressor in the engine room, which also houses the CP powered combined pump set.

In the cooling compartment are two Reavell motor-driven rotary vacuum exhausters for train brake operation. This system is compressed-air controlled from the driver's automatic air brake valve. This permits haulage of Continental railway rolling stock, which is air-braked, without running the vacuum exhauster. An anti-slip brake button is fitted in the power control handle.

Pending the arrival of class 33, as we have already seen, the SR borrowed class 24 locomotives from the LMR, D6500 arriving at Hither Green depot in December 1959. By late summer 1960, some 18 locomotives had been delivered and were in use on Kent coast traffic out of Charing Cross. By September all the London–Dover through trains were in their hands, although their lack of steam-heating and the lack of eth-equipped rolling stock caused problems when winter set in. The practice of working in multiple with a class 24 to provide steam heating was instigated.

As the only eth-equipped BR diesels, they were curiosities to other regions, but D6504 was lent to the LMR at Derby in early 1961 for static and running tests. Runs were made from Derby to Hornsey (GN), via Peterborough, and on the East Coast main line between King's Cross and

Well away from home, class 33 D6577 leaves York for the south with the one-time regular Uddingston (Glasgow)–Holborough (SR) round trip bulk cement train in September 1962. This type of locomotive was used on the York–Holborough section of the service.

(Brian Webb)

Edinburgh (Craigentinny). D6553 was also lent to Derby in January 1964, in this case for Freightliner trials, being chosen for its type of air-brake. Dynamometer trials were run to Leicester, the locomotive returning to the SR later that month.

SR duties included the Sunday 'Golden Arrow', running via Chatham with two class 33s in multiple, while their most interesting inter-regional duty began in December 1961. This was the 02.30 class C bulk cement train between Holborough (SR) and Uddingston (ScR). This train of 28 tankers was hauled initially as far as York with two class 33s, and later with one. Occasionally the locomotives worked through to Scotland.

Hither Green depot had all 98 locomotives based there for maintenance, but in practice the class worked many depots' duties. In April 1963, D6504 was lent to Eastleigh for trials on Fawley branch freight duties, and by summer many were on loan to Eastleigh, working Waterloo–Bournemouth and Southampton boat trains along with the Bulleid Pacifics. Other duties, such as Fawley–Bromford Bridge oil trains, took them to Saltley depot, Birmingham, for overnight stays. In December 1964, the locomotives were allocated as follows:

Eastleigh: D6504–6/12/20/1/3–8/30/3–7/40/1/ 5/6/9/56/78/83/5

Hither Green: D6500/1/3/7–11/3–9/22/9/31/ 2/8/9/42–4/7/8/50–5/7–77/9–82/4

St Leonards: D6586–97 (narrow locomotives)

The coming of the Bournemouth electrification brought a requirement to equip locomotives for push-and-pull operation and a number of class 33s were included. D6580 was fitted in mid-1965, and put on tests with a six-coach trailer-controlled set (6TC) between Wimbledon and Basingstoke, along with similar tests with an electro-diesel locomotive also push-and-pull fitted. Similar tests on the Oxted line were carried out early in 1966 using D6580 and trains from Victoria, and London Bridge to East Grinstead. By early 1967 Eastleigh had fitted 19 locomotives with waist-level jumpers and buckeye couplers, these being D6511/3/4/6/7/9/20/1/5/7–9/31–3/5/ 6/80.

From the summer of 1967 unreliability of the WR Warship diesel-hydraulics on the Waterloo–Exeter services saw class 33 deputising singly or in multiple, or with the rostered Warship diesel. This was a pointer to the 1971 changeover from the latter, on 4 October 1971, the use of ten-year-old locomotives on top link duties! Loads of eight coaches were well within the capacity of the 33s. In 1971 a start was made in fitting a batch of 33s with SSC for use on mgr coal trains to power stations in the region.

Three class 33 have been withdrawn: D6502 in May 1964, after two freight trains collided at Itchingfield Junction on 5 March 1964; D6575, involved in a collision at Reading, withdrawn in November 1968; and 33041 in November 1975 after a collision in September at Bricklayers Arms Junction.

The second batch of BRCW type 2 locomotives was considerably different from the first 47 locomotives. They were numbered D5347–D5415. In this case the engine is the Sulzer 6LDA28-B unit of 1250bhp; electrical equipment is by General Electric Co. Ltd (GEC) and the locomotives are accordingly classified 27. A GEC model WT981 main generator is used. This is a ten-pole machine with four field windings: separately excited, self-excited, reverse series and starting. It is rated at

The 14.00 to Waterloo, headed by class 33 loco-motives in multiple D6578 and D6579, at Exeter St Davids on 8 August 1971. *(Norman E. Preedy)*

805kW, 1940A, at 750rpm. Mounted on the same hub is a GEC auxiliary generator of 57kW and type WT782. This is a six-pole machine with automatically maintained 110V output. Both generators are self-ventilated.

Four GEC WT459 axle-hung nose-suspended traction motors are fitted, being connected in parallel. Each motor has a rating of 236hp at 485A, 415V, and single-reduction gear drive with Wiseman gears and a ratio of 17:60. These loco-motives are geared for a maximum speed of 90mph compared to 75mph for D5300–46, their maximum power being available at higher speeds than their precedessors, in fact up to 80mph. This was achieved by a combination of generator voltage control and motor field control.

Auxiliaries include an electrically-driven radia-tor fan of 840/1500rpm under thermostat con-trol. Two-speed Aerex-Hyperform twin-blowers cool the traction motors. The blowers and radia-tor fan motors run at high speed when a certain controller position is reached, thus reducing loading on auxiliary generator at low engine speeds. Two Northey two-speed vacuum-exhaus-ters are fitted. These maintain vacuum at low speed but increase in speed as brake release under control of the brake valve approaches. A West-inghouse air-compressor provides air for control and locomotive braking. The engine water and oil pumps are driven from the battery for starting purposes, and will maintain required oil and water circulation after shutting down of the diesel engine. A Stone-Vapor steam-generator was fitted originally in all except D5370–8 for train-heating. The Nife batteries are contained in two roll-out boxes on each side of the locomotive underframe. The main water and fuel tanks are also hung from the underframe, but the train-heating water tank and service fuel tanks are roof-mounted inside the locomotive.

The bogies were modified from those fitted to D5300–46. Their secondary suspension in this case has nests of coil springs, and the bolsters have a shock absorber at each end to overcome vertical riding problems experienced with D5300–46 on indifferent track. Traction motor bellows were improved to ensure constant contact with the ducting and avoid dirt entering the traction motors.

Improvements in accessibility of equipment were made, and the cab interior designed to improve comfort and make maintenance and cleaning easier. Their mechanical portion was improved so that the cab front gangways were less draughty and the engine room roof of trans-lucent glass-fibre was fitted with quick-release fittings. A four-digit indicator box was provided on the cab roof.

During 1970 tests were conducted with loco-motives of classes 37, 47 and 50 for a proposed high-speed Inter-City push-and-pull service be-tween Glasgow and Edinburgh. Motorway com-petition and the obsolescence of the 1957 Swin-don-built six-car diesel-mechanical railcar sets had made improvements necessary, although at their introduction these units had considerably lifted passenger receipts. They ran non-stop or stopping on two routes, via Falkirk (High) or Falkirk (Grahamston). Due to a shortage of classes 37, 47 and 50, coupled with the reluctance of their users to let them go, the unusual choice of a pair of class 27 locomotives was made, one each end of a rake of six Mk II carriages. Owing to the high speeds required, and expected high-speed braking, locomotives with air-operated disc brakes were required, plus facilities for electric train heating. Single-manning with control from the cab of whichever locomotive was leading meant through locomotive engine control and warning systems. Twenty-four locomotives and 36 coaches were needed to meet the operating requirements of five sets, leaving six coaches and four locomotives spare. To meet the locomotive requirements 12 class 27 were sent to Derby works from September 1970 to be modified in the following ways:

(a) Steam generators removed and replaced by a separate 130kW alternator set powered by a Deutz diesel engine.
(b) BR dual-braking system fitted.
(c) Automatic fire-fighting equipment was needed on unmanned locomotives at rear of train. This operated automatically once engine room temperatures reached 120°C.
(d) Driver-guard communication system fitted.
(e) Traction generators and traction motors overhauled and re-wound.

St Rollox works dealt with the other 12 locomotives, which were overhauled and modified to supply eth from their traction generator group; a separate eth supply was not fitted. Tests were carried out from Derby works with push-and-pull sets prior to the equipment returning to Scotland. D5404/7 were involved on the Midland line between Derby and Leicester in March 1971. Regular push-and-pull services on the Glasgow–Edinburgh route started in May 1971. Almost immediately problems started with the locomotives, and frequent substitution by various non push-and-pull locomotives resulted over many months.

The use of general-purpose locomotives for such onerous duties with prolonged high-speed running gave rise to many faults. As a result of this, traction motor bandings had to be strengthened, commutator covers were lost at speed, and experiments took some time to find suitable permanent replacements, which were unusually of fire-proofed chip-board. Brake gear had to be modified, the bogie primary coil spring suspension bolts replaced by stronger ones of tensile steel. Traction motor suspensions were modified, while in 1971 a spate of flashovers was traced to vibrations affecting the brush gear due to wear at fixing points; high-speed running and braking forces were blamed for this.

By summer 1972 many problems had been overcome, but not all, for generator insulation failures were experienced and the Deutz alternator set started to give problems in 1976 when the engine in 27 207 seized up due to overheating.

This was put down to cooling air being recirculated; to overcome this a new partition was fitted and testing carried out at Derby in April/May 1976. Another problem caused by heat was the failure of Deutz engine dampers which were of rubber-sandwich type. It was thought that the partition would also overcome this problem.

Traction motor suspension failures occurred again in 1976, and new bearings were to be fitted at St Rollox. Early 1977 found the service hard-pressed for locomotives due to generator problems. Driving gear-wheel breakages on the push-and-pull locomotives caused failures in classes 27/1 and 27/2. New David Brown gears were fitted and the removed reuseable Wiseman gears kept as spares for class 27/0 which operate on less demanding duties than the push-and-pull locomotives. Further problems with severe wear on top brake-hanger brackets caused special modifications on three class 27/1 locomotives. Extended welded-on bosses and brackets were fitted as an experiment to see if these provided the solution.

Engine troubles with the class 26 and 27 locomotives in recent years have been slight, although cases of broken cylinder head studs were reported in early 1976.

In the earlier years the phenomena of unequal cylinder liner wear in the 6LDA28 engine fitted in both the BR-built classes 24/25 and the BRCW-built class 26 led to investigations. It was decided to compare the effectiveness of the engine room air intake filters. Six locomotives of each type working from Inverness depot in Scotland were chosen for a period of test observation. The filter elements were weighed in clean condition, after oil-wetting, and again at set times during the locomotives' service. In the BR-built locomotives, with their filters in the bodyside main members, it was discovered that the four lower-mounted filters on each side were so filthy as to allow dirt to enter the locomotive, and thereby the engine combustion air. The BRCW locomotives, with their much higher placed filters above cant rail, were much superior. This resulted in the adoption of this type for later batches of BR class 25 locomotives.

Water treatment of engine coolant water caused many problems with corrosion in all BR diesel classes. Magnesium alloy liners were first used to prevent engine waterway corrosion. These liners, as cylindrical segments, were clamped round the cylinder liners preventing corrosion, except that the segments corroded

Top: Class 26/1 26 030, with cabside recess for tablet exchange apparatus, in multiple with class 27/0 27 029 with a load of coal from the Waterside exchange sidings of the steam-worked NCB system there on 2 September 1975. *(Brian Webb)*

Above: Class 26/0 Sulzer–Crompton Parkinson equipped 1160bhp locomotive 26 003 traverses Princes Street Gardens, Edinburgh, with a down cement train in June 1975. Note that cabside doors have their windows sheeted over and that the corridor connection is welded up. *(Fred Kerr)*

Right: D5341 climbs through the Kingswood Forest between Dunkeld & Birnam and Murthly on the Highland main line with an Inverness–Perth freight on 3 October 1968. *(John M. Boyes)*

away! Due to the short life of these liner segments water treatment was recommended. Water treatment in its turn brought problems by attacking rubber components in the engine cooling system. Further trials with variations in coolant and types of rubbers eventually largely overcame this problem.

Although in 1977 all the surviving locomotives of classes 26/27 were allocated to the ScR, this

One of the then NER Thornaby-based class 27, D5372 passing York Holgate platforms with a northbound freight. These locomotives, D5370–8, were built without train-heating boilers. 25 August 1962.

(Brian Webb)

was not originally so. The first 20 locomotives (D5300–19) were allocated to Hornsey depot on the ER for use on suburban work out of King's Cross, D5300 being accepted at Doncaster works and arriving at Hornsey during July 1958. Until their move to Scotland in 1960, they worked suburban trains from King's Cross and Moorgate, King's Cross–Grimsby trains, and to Cambridge, etc., plus freight duties. This was indeed fortunate, due to the great shortcomings of another type based in the area. The Scottish Region was allocated D5320–46, the first being accepted at Doncaster in April 1959. However, D5330–35 were lent to the ER in 1959 to overcome locomotive shortages. D5320–46 were allocated to Edinburgh Haymarket depot, but lack of facilities for diesels saw them kept at Leith Central railcar depot for a period. Their early life appeared leisurely, being mostly crew training and runs to Dundee and Perth on freight and fish trains. In late 1959, D5337/8 were tested on the Edinburgh–Aberdeen route with 11 carriages and the Hallade track-recording coach. In early 1960, D5338–46 moved on to Inverness, to be followed by locomotives brought to Aberdeen (Ferryhill) and Perth for training purposes. In March 1960 the class took on the Edinburgh–Aberdeen trains, running very well on the 3hr 8min timings; they were replaced by class 40 2000hp locomotives in 1962. Once Haymarket received the 20 ER locomotives, D5320–37 were transferred to Inverness, being soon employed on Highland section duties, taking on many Glasgow–Aberdeen trains. The Waverley line saw many class 26 on Edinburgh–Hawick and Carlisle freight and passenger duties.

In 1966 the first seven class 26, D5300–6, were fitted with ssc for working on the mgr coal trains to Cockenzie power station. At the same time the steam generators for train-heating were removed and a larger air-compressor fitted for air-braking of the mgr trains. This was later replaced by two

The Sulzer–GEC equipped class 27 have all ended up in the Scottish Region. Here D5401 is seen west of Lochailort with the 16.40 Fort William–Mallaig mixed train in April 1973.   *(Peter W. Robinson)*

compressors from withdrawn class 24 locomotives. Plans to withdraw 12 of the class in 1977 would have provided much needed spares for the surviving locomotives.

The D5347–D5415 series was built in 1961/2 and allocated as follows: ScR—D5347–69; NER —D5370–8; LMR—D5379–D5415. D5347 was accepted at Doncaster in June 1961, going along with the whole of the Scottish batch initially to Glasgow Eastfield depot for West Highland line duties. The NER batch did not have steam-generators, as they were for freight duties from Thornaby depot, being allocated there until January 1966, when they went to the LMR in exchange for class 25 locomotives. While on the NER they often worked in multiple on East Coast main line freights. They weighed only 71ton 4cwt compared to 72ton 10cwt for the remainder. D5379–D5415 went to the Midland lines of the LMR at Cricklewood shed, where they mainly worked freight duties, but did stints on St Pancras suburban trains and empty carriage duties. By May 1962 the locomotives were working multiple on some St Pancras–Nottingham trains, followed by work on the 'Condor' container trains. Their work continued to expand onto mineral trains to and from Wellingborough, then onto Marylebone–Nottingham trains. D5403 was lent to the ER at March depot in August 1963 for training purposes prior to the class taking up workings to Whitemoor later that year. As part of a standardisation programme all the BRCW type 2 locomotives finished up in Scotland by 1970, being exchanged for class 25 and class 20 locomotives.

The premature withdrawal of the class 26/27 due to collisions and fires has not been large, but D5383, then based at Cricklewood LMR, was withdrawn in January 1966 after involvement in a collision of two freight trains at East Langton, near Market Harborough, on 20 August 1965.

Since 1970 the Scottish locomotives have continued on their mixed duties on West Highland and Highland line duties, including the Oban line. Along with their BR-built brethren, the BRCW Sulzers have earned a good reputation for all-round reliability, and their reputation after other types have both come and gone would seem to uphold this. The 26s are being pushed to their limits as they approach withdrawal by the coincidence of the great rise in Highland freight traffic, due to the North Sea oil boom, and the locomotive shortages due to falling availability of classes 26 and 27.

TABLE 9   MAIN VARIATIONS IN CLASSES 26, 27 AND 33 Bo-Bo DIESEL ELECTRICS BASED ON BRITISH RAIL DIAGRAM BOOK MT25 OF 1974

Number series	26 001–46	26 001–46	26 001–46	27 001–44	27 001–44	27 101–12	27 113–24⁵
Former number series	D5300–46	D5300–46	D5300–46	D5347–5415	D5347–5415	D5347–5415	D5347–5415
Class	26/0	26/0	26/1	27/0	27/0	27/1	27/1
Diagram number	26aX	26bV	26/1aV	27aV	27bV	27/1aX	27/1bX
Weight in working order	73ton 17cwt	77ton 17cwt	73ton 6cwt	73ton 6cwt	71ton 4cwt	76ton 1cwt	75ton 9cwt
Fuel capacity, gal	500	500¹	500²	500³	600	684⁴	970
Boiler water capacity, gal	—	550	450	450	—	300	—
Generator type	CP CG391A1	CP CG391A1	CP CG391A1	GEC WT981	GEC WT981	GEC WT981	GEC WT981
Traction motor type	CP C171A1	CP C171A1	CP C171D3	GEC WT459	GEC WT459	GEC WT459	GEC WT459
Rail hp	900	900	900	933	933	933	933
Maximum tractive effort, lb	42,000	42,000	42,000	40,000	40,000	40,000	40,000
Continuous tractive effort, lb/mph	30,000/11·25	30,000/11·25	30,000/11·25	25,000/14·0	25,000/14·0	25,000/14·0	25,000/14·0
Train heating { Boiler type	—	Vapor OK4625	Vapor OK4625	Vapor OK4625	—	Vapor OK4625	—
Train heating { Eth	—	—	—	—	—	—	—
Braking { Locomotive	SA AA	A	A	A	A	SA AA	SA AA
Braking { Train	AA ACV	V	V	V	V	AA ACV	AA ACV

Notes: ¹, ², ³ and ⁴ Boiler fuel 100 gallons.   ⁵ 27 113–24 renumbered 27 201–12, diagram 27/1bX becoming obsolete. For full details of individual locomotive renumbering see Table No. 12.

TABLE 10
WORKS NUMBERS AND DATES INTO RUNNING STOCK FOR BRCW-BUILT CLASS 26 AND 27 Bo-Bo DIESEL-ELECTRIC LOCOMOTIVES

Number	Builder	Works No.	Date	Region
D5300	BRCW	DEL45	7/58	E
D5301	BRCW	DEL46	9/58	E
D5302–4	BRCW	DEL47–9	10/58	E
D5305/6	BRCW	DEL50/1	11/58	E
D5307–9	BRCW	DEL52–4	12/58	E
D5310–4	BRCW	DEL55–9	1/59	E
D5315–7	BRCW	DEL60–2	2/59	E
D5318/9	BRCW	DEL63/4	3/59	E
D5320/1	BRCW	DEL65/6	P 4/59	Sc
D5322–5	BRCW	DEL67–70	P 5/59	Sc
D5326–9	BRCW	DEL71–4	P 6/59	Sc
D5330–3	BRCW	DEL75–8	P 7/59	Sc
D5334/5	BRCW	DEL79/80	P 8/59	Sc
D5336–9	BRCW	DEL81–4	P 9/59	Sc
D5340–3	BRCW	DEL85–8	P10/59	Sc
D5344–6	BRCW	DEL89–91	P11/59	Sc
D5347	BRCW	DEL190	P 7/61	Sc
D5348/9	BRCW	DEL191/2	P 8/61	Sc
D5350–2	BRCW	DEL193–5	P 9/61	Sc
D5353–5	BRCW	DEL196–8	P10/61	Sc
D5356–9	BRCW	DEL199–202	P11/61	Sc
D5360–2	BRCW	DEL203–5	P12/61	Sc
D5363–5	BRCW	DEL206–8	P13/61	Sc
D5366–9	BRCW	DEL209–12	P 1/62	Sc

Number	Builder	Works No.	Date	Region
D5370–3	BRCW	DEL213–6	1/62	NE
D5374–7	BRCW	DEL217–20	2/62	NE
D5378	BRCW	DEL221	3/62	NE
D5379–82	BRCW	DEL222–5	P 4/62	LM
D5383–6	BRCW	DEL226–9	P 5/62	LM
D5387–92	BRCW	DEL230–5	P 6/62	LM
D5393–6	BRCW	DEL236–9	P 7/62	LM
D5397	BRCW	DEL240	P 8/62	LM
D5398–D5402	BRCW	DEL241–5	P 7/62	LM
D5403–7	BRCW	DEL246–50	P 8/62	LM
D5408	BRCW	DEL251	P 9/62	LM
D5409	BRCW	DEL252	P 8/62	LM
D5410–2	BRCW	DEL253–5	P 9/62	LM
D5413–5	BRCW	DEL256–8	P10/62	LM

TABLE 11
WORKS NUMBERS AND DATES INTO RUNNING STOCK FOR BRCW-BUILT CLASS 33 Bo-Bo DIESEL-ELECTRIC LOCOMOTIVES

Number	Builder	Works No.	Date	Region
D6500	BRCW	DEL92	1/60	S
D6501	BRCW	DEL93	2/60	S
D6502–4	BRCW	DEL94–6	3/60	S
D6505–6	BRCW	DEL97/8	4/60	S
D6507–9	BRCW	DEL99–101	5/60	S
D6510–3	BRCW	DEL102–5	6/60	S
D6514–7	BRCW	DEL106–9	7/60	S
D6518/9	BRCW	DEL110/1	8/60	S
D6520–3	BRCW	DEL112–5	9/60	S
D6524–8	BRCW	DEL116–20	10/60	S

27 201–12	33 001–65	33 101–19	33 201–12
D5347–5415	D6500–97	D6500–97	D6500–97
27/2	33/0	33/1	33/2
27/2aX	33aX	33/1aX	33/2aX
75ton 11cwt	76ton 9cwt	77ton 6cwt	76ton 5cwt
970	800	800	800
—	—	—	—
GEC WT981	CP CG391B1	CP CG391B1	CP CG391B1
GEC WT459	CP171C2	CP171C2	CP171C2
933	1215	1215	1215
40,000	45,000	45,000	45,000
25,000/14·0	26,000/17·5	26,000/17·5	26,000/17·5
—	—	—	—
Deutz eth	CP	CP	CP
SA AA AA ACV	SA AA AA ACV	SA AA AA ACV	SA AA AA ACV

Original No.	Renumbering	Later became
D5320	26 028	
D5321–7	26 021–7	
D5328	withdrawn	
D5329–46	26 029–46	
D5347–73	27 001–27	
D5374	27 101	
D5375–9	27 028–32	
D5380	27 102	
D5381/2	27 033/4	
D5383	withdrawn	
D5384/5	27 035/6	
D5386–8	27 103–5	
D5389/90	27 037/8	
D5391–3	27 119–21	27 201–3
D5394–7	27 106–9	
D5398	27 039	
D5399–D5401	27 110–2	
D5402	27 040	
D5403	27 122	27 204
D5404	27 113	27 207
D5405/6	27 041/2	
D5407–9	27 114–6	27 208–10
D5410	27 123	27 205
D5411	27 117	27 211
D5412	27 124	27 206
D5413	27 118	27 212
D5414/5	27 043/4	

Locomotives shown as withdrawn were not allocated new numbers.

D6529–32	BRCW	DEL121–4	11/60	S
D6533–7	BRCW	DEL125–9	12/60	S
D6538–41	BRCW	DEL130–3	1/61	S
D6542–4	BRCW	DEL134–6	2/61	S
D6545–7	BRCW	DEL137–9	3/61	S
D6548–52	BRCW	DEL140–4	4/61	S
D6553–5	BRCW	DEL145–7	5/61	S
D6556–9	BRCW	DEL148–51	6/61	S
D6560–4	BRCW	DEL152–6	7/61	S
D6565/6	BRCW	DEL169/70	8/61	S
D6567–70	BRCW	DEL171–4	9/61	S
D6571/2	BRCW	DEL175/6	10/61	S
D6573	BRCW	DEL177	11/61	S
D6574	BRCW	DEL178	10/61	S
D6575–8	BRCW	DEL179–82	11/61	S
D6579–82	BRCW	DEL183–6	12/61	S
D6583–5	BRCW	DEL187–9	1/62	S
D6586–90	BRCW	DEL157–61	2/62	S
D6591–4	BRCW	DEL162–5	3/62	S
D6595/6	BRCW	DEL166/7	4/62	S
D6597	BRCW	DEL168	5/62	S

TABLE 12
RENUMBERING OF BRCW-BUILT Bo-Bo
DIESEL-ELECTRICS OF CLASSES 26 AND 27

Original No.	Renumbering	Later became
D5300	26 020	
D5301–19	26 001–19	

TABLE 13
RENUMBERING OF BRCW-BUILT Bo-Bo
DIESEL-ELECTRICS OF CLASS 33

Original No.	Renumbering
D6500/1	33 001/2
D6502	withdrawn
D6503–10	33 003–10
D6511	33 101
D6512	33 012
D6513/4	33 102/3
D6515	33 013
D6516/7	33 104/5
D6518	33 014
D6519–21	33 106–8
D6522–4	33 015–7
D6525	33 109
D6526	33 018
D6527–9	33 110–2
D6530	33 019
D6531–3	33 113–5
D6534	33 020
D6535/6	33 116/7
D6537	33 021
D6538	33 118
D6539–75	33 022–58
D6576	withdrawn
D6577–9	33 059–61
D6580	33 119
D6581–5	33 062–6
D6586–97	33 201–12

Locomotives shown as withdrawn were not allocated new numbers.

CHAPTER 6

THE BRUSH SULZER — CLASS 47

The so-called BR 'standard type 4' diesel-electric locomotive is in fact no such thing. It was ordered in quantity straight from the drawing board to meet the obsessive rush to dieselisation adopted by BR. Thus it had to be developed while in production until a total of 512 locomotives had been built.

Its origin lay in a desire for locomotives of lower weight and higher power than the 1Co-Co1 133–138-ton 2000–2500bhp units currently in production, ie locomotives that could be carried on two six-wheel bogies in which all axles were powered. Ignoring the massive plate-frame 1Co bogies, the 1Co-Co1 locomotives were the result of conservative thinking and the fears of the BR civil engineers of rail breakages. The result was designs with axle-weight to wheel diameter ratios of 4:5, or less. The problems of the 1Co bogie on sharp curves and on vertical curves in marshalling yards were accepted at the time, but posed problems in yards without escape roads avoiding the humps.

Thoughts on a possible Co-Co design of 114–115 tons and 2700–2800bhp gained substance when the 1959 order placed with Brush for class 46 power equipments was cut by 20 sets of equipment for installation in a Co-Co design. At the same time the Sulzer twin-bank engine was available as a 2750bhp unit so, in collaboration with the BR Design Panel, Brush Electrical was given the job of designing such a Co-Co locomotive to meet future requirements, within specifications laid down by BR, making use of the 20 sets of equipment in hand.

The obvious requirement by BR of a large number of such locomotives caused the production by the British locomotive industry of three prototype diesel electrics, of which one was built within the BR specification. Brush was first in the field with its Co-Co of 2800bhp in 1961. This 115-ton unit, named *Falcon* and numbered D0280, was a unique locomotive because, at the time of its design, there was no single diesel engine of sufficient power to give the output required so, no doubt influenced by the BR Western class 2700bhp diesel-hydraulics, a twin-engine/generator combination using the same Bristol-Siddeley Maybach engines as the diesel-hydraulic was produced. *Falcon* had two 1400bhp engines of MD655 type running at 1500rpm. Each engine drove its own generator group and supplied power to three Brush traction motors on one bogie. Apart from the specialised EE 3300bhp Deltic locomotives on the East Coast main line, no other twin-engine high-power diesel-electric has run on BR. Built at Loughborough alongside the BR Brush type 2 A1A-A1A locomotives, *Falcon* owes nothing to that design, with its heavy underframe and body with detachable sides, but was rather a locomotive with an integral body structure. The body was of load-bearing, open-girder type, the locomotive running on two Commonwealth cast steel bogies. *Falcon* did, however, point to the way in which BR type 4 thinking was heading.

The original class 47 D1500, in its present form as 47 401, with an up express at Peterborough on 20 May 1977. *(John A. Howie)*

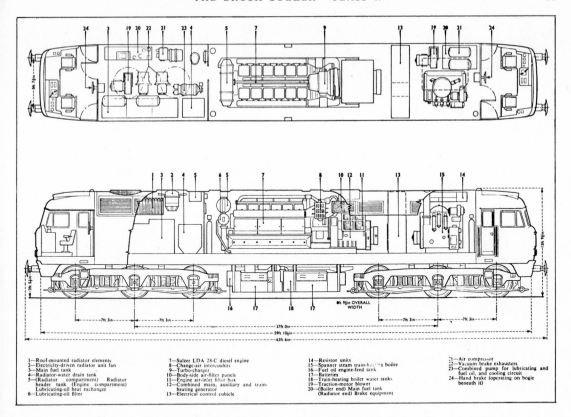

1—Roof-mounted radiator elements	7—Sulzer LDA 28-C diesel engine
2—Electricity-driven radiator unit fan	8—Change-air intercoolers
3—Main fuel tank	9—Turbo-charger
4—Radiator-water drain tank	10—Body-side air-filter panels
5—(Radiator compartment) Radiator header tank (Engine compartment) Lubricating-oil heat exchanger	11—Engine air-inlet filter box
	12—Combined main, auxiliary and train-heating generator
6—Lubricating-oil filter	13—Electrical control cubicle

14—Resistor units	21—Air compressor
15—Spanner steam train-heating boiler	22—Vacuum brake exhausters
16—Fuel oil engine-feed tank	23—Combined pump for lubricating and fuel oil, and cooling circuit
17—Batteries	24—Hand brake (operating on bogie beneath it)
18—Train-heating boiler water tanks	
19—Traction-motor blower	
20—(Boiler end) Main fuel tank (Radiator end) Brake equipment	

Above: Equipment layout diagram of class 47 2750bhp Co-Co diesel-electric locomotives D1500–19. (*Collection of B. Webb*)

Below: Side and end elevation of class 47. (*British Railways*)

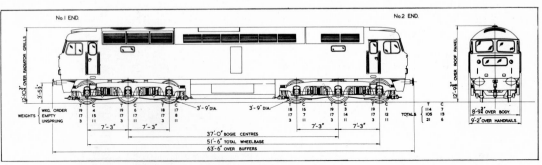

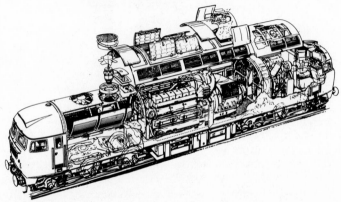

Left: Exploded view of class 47 D1500–19 series. (*Brush Electrical Machines*)

Second of the prototypes to appear was the EE locomotive DP2 which entered service in May 1962. DP2 was not a new design, as it made use of the mechanical portion of the BR Deltic locomotives, so perpetuating the large high bulbous nose of its parent, and in this respect it was certainly not in accord with contemporary BR thought. DP2 weighed 10 tons less than *Falcon* at 105 tons, in spite of its use of the bulky EE 16CSVT 2700bhp engine with 16 cylinders, running at 850rpm. This highly successful locomotive was not favoured by BR, which was by then already committing itself to the Brush-Sulzer Co-Co then under way at Loughborough, but ironically the final batch of 50 BR type 4 Co-Co locomotives turned out to be a new EE design with flat-front cab using DP2's engine and EE electrical equipment. These were the class 50 locomotives of 1967/8.

The third prototype was built within the BR type 4 specification and used the Sulzer 2750bhp engine. This was the 1962 locomotive *Lion*. This locomotive, D0260, was built by BRCW-Sulzer-AEI, and is covered in Chapter 7.

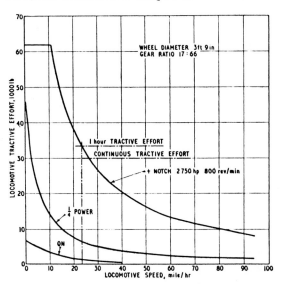

Class 47 Speed/tractive effort curve.

So a 2750bhp Co-Co of the required weight materialised from Brush. But before any appeared the design was made available to British locomotive builders as the subject of competitive tendering. In the event Brush got the lot and BR Crewe works was also licensed to build them. This was the first time a privately, or at least part privately, designed diesel main line locomotive had been built in railway workshops.

The Brush-Sulzer type 4—hereafter referred to as class 47—was not simply the result of replacing the two small engines of *Falcon* with one of Sulzer type. Firstly the combined weight of its two Maybach engines with generators was only 13·8 tons, but the Sulzer twin-bank engine weighed, with its generator, 22 tons. Considerable variation in component weights gave interesting comparisons: *Falcon*'s body weighed 21·5 tons (0·330 tons per foot), the class 47 body, 17 tons (0·285 tons per foot), and in only engine, boiler and water tanks, fuel, sand and water supplies did the class 47 weigh more than *Falcon*.

The class 47 did not use a conventional underframe, but the whole of the body, excluding cabs, was built on monocoque principles as a fully load-bearing structure, taking advantage of the Hawker-Siddeley Aviation division and its experience in stressed-skin construction. Body strength lies in the bodyside framing, the linking cross-stretchers, continuous sheet-steel floor decking plate, compartment bulkheads and roof sections. Only a few structural items are non-load bearing, roof areas over engine, etc., plus some bracketing and support rails. Vertical and end loads are taken by the bodyside built up from rolled-steel sections, panelled with sheet steel which is stiffened with folded sections to resist buckling. The floor plate, in addition to its share of loading, also serves as a waste sump under the engine. Traction and vertical loads are transferred from bogie pivots and engine mountings through box-section cross-stretchers to the bodysides; these also provide jacking points. Buffing/drawing loads are passed to the whole structure by dragboxes at both ends, via a triangular framework inside the locomotive cabs which passes loads over the cab doorway to the bodysides. This framework does to some extent affect drivers' access when looking out of the cabside windows. Testing by strain gauges proved successful with 200-ton buffing loads.

The cab itself is fitted separately, and is made from aluminium castings, extruded sections and sheeting, a glass-fibre moulded roof canopy being used. The cab and its rear bulkhead is insulated against noise and cold. A wooden floor covered with linoleum is used in both cabs. Each cab has standard BR layout and equipment common to other diesel locomotives, but a summary in this instance is useful. Each cab has a left-hand driving position, and second man position to its right, both with chairs. The main controls are on a

Body structure of D1500 on the test-rig for body loading tests and with the Sulzer twin-bank engine being lowered in, at the works of Brush Traction, Loughborough, in 1962. *(Brush Electrical Machines)*

desk/console in front of the driver. These are main ammeter, speedometer, power-controller, braking valves, and various gauges, warning lights and indicators, including engine-stopped and wheel-slip indicators, all within easy reach and vision. The deadman treadle is supplemented by a button at second man position. The cab is electrically heated, and a food warmer is fitted in the locomotive.

A very clean exterior body design has been achieved by grouping all grilles above cant-rail level or in the roof sections—ie., radiator mountings, ductings, fan cowls, motor supports, in radiator roof sections, and filters for air in lower sides of the roof. Non load-bearing roof areas are removable from cant-level and are of aluminium or translucent glass-fibre. Four hinged hatches open outwards above the engine for top access and others come out for turbo-charger and heat exchanger attention. Roof-mounted radiators by Serck are used; the first 20 locomotives (D1500–19) have electrically-driven fans with their own motors, but all the remainder have Serck-Behr hydrostatic oil-motors driven by an engine-driven hydrostatic pump. Considerable modification was necessary to meet this change and brought in its wake oil leaks due to vibration at oil seals. The electric drive was preferred by maintenance staff.

Filtration of engine, generator, control and traction motor air is through metal oil-wetted filters at cant level in the train-heating boiler compartment and engine compartment. Engine air is additionally filtered through an air filter box over the generator group. Traction motor blower air is provided by two blowers, one in the boiler and the other in the radiator compartment, each supplying the adjacent bogie via ducting and flexible bellows.

D1500–19 were fitted with both steam train heating, from a Spanner Swirlyflow Mk III steam generator, and eth, these items being a large factor in the locomotives' weight reaching 117 tons rather than 114/5 tons. Later class 47s had only steam heating, apart from locomotives intended for freight work, which have none. Water tanks for train-heating are underhung from the locomotive between the bogies. Balancing pipes are fitted, as are steam heating coils where boilers are fitted, to prevent freezing.

In order to meet regional requirements, from 1964 the fitting of a 'universal' boiler compartment was initiated. This compartment was laid out to receive any one of four steam generators of three different makes: Spanner, Clayton and Stone-Vapor. Locomotives built without boilers carried a 35cwt ballast weight to maintain weight distribution and locomotive adhesion. There are three fuel tanks, two main and a measuring tank, supplying the engine. The main tanks are on resilient mountings on the floor of the radiator and boiler compartments, the measuring tank rigidly on one water tank. Battery boxes, four in number, are slung under the locomotive.

Bogies of Commonwealth cast-steel type, made of manganese steel for lightness, are fitted. These have sprung, swing bolsters with coil primary and secondary spring suspension. Secondary spring damping is by hydraulic dampers between the bolsters and spring planks at each nest. The bogie frames are supported by four nests of double-coil springs, mounted on forged steel underslung equalising beams, which are suspended from beneath the axleboxes by pins and rubber bushes at the outer ends, and by stirrups with rubber sandwiches at the inner axleboxes. Axleboxes are cast-steel with manganese liners on their guiding faces and fitted with Hoffmann parallel, SKF tapered, or Timken tapered roller bearings. During 1963 new axleboxes with redesigned wheelsets were made necessary due to cracking under the wheelsets. New traction motor suspension bearings are of roller type; not all locomotives having the same make. Originally all suspension tubes were interchangeable, but modifications to some Timken units made traction motor modifications necessary, thereby losing full standardisation. D1500–19 are fitted, ten with Timken suspension tubes, and ten with Hoffmann tubes and bearings, as are D1520–49. Apart from 110 locomotives in the D1550–1999/D1100–11 series, these all have Hoffmann tubes and bearings but of split type. The 100 locomotives, numbered from D1862 up, received SKF suspension tubes and bearings.

Traction and braking loads transfer from the axles of the bogie frames by guiding faces on the axleboxes and horn guides on the frames; these in turn transfer the loads to the superstructure. All rubbing, traction faces and pivots have renewable manganese liners.

Air brakes are provided on the locomotives; train braking was vacuum, but the adoption of air-braking has seen this progressively fitted to provide the dual-brake facility. The locomotive power-brake system incorporates an anti-slip brake operated by a push-button in the driver's power handle in the cab; some later locomotives have this button on the control desk.

Auxiliary equipment varies considerably from batch to batch. D1500–19 have two traction motor blowers of series-wound inter-polar type connected in permanent series. These have a continuous rating of 11·9bhp, 355V, 30A, at 1855rpm. In D1520–1999/D1100–11 the blowers are inter-polar, but connected separately and wound to 110V to suit the auxiliary generator, but still giving 11·9hp at 1855rpm. Both batches have inter-polar series-wound vacuum exhauster motors rated at 4·25hp at 1250rpm supplied from the auxiliary generator. The exhausters themselves are by Northey. D1500–19 have Westinghouse air compressors; the remainder, Brush-powered Davies and Metcalfe-Oerlikon units.

The locomotives are fitted with the Sulzer 12LDA28C twin-bank diesel engine originally rated at 2750bhp, but now operating at 2580bhp.

The Brush main generator varies from batch to batch. On D1500–19 it is model TG 160-60 Mk II developed from that applied to class 46. At 1150rpm it is continuously-rated at 1798kW, 844V, 2130A; one-hour rating is 1805kW, 970V, 1860A. It is an eight-pole three-field unit, with separately excited, self-excited, shunt-windings, and a series decompounding field. The series winding also acts for engine starting. On the common hub are also carried the auxiliary and electric train heating generators. The former is a 16-pole shunt-wound unit with a nominal voltage of 110, a carbon-pile automatic voltage regulator maintaining this over required load and speed range. The continuous rating is 264kW, 110V, 240A. This combined machine was 4800lb heavier than those fitted in later locomotives.

Electric train heating is provided by an eight-pole shunt-wound machine with an output of 800V automatically maintained. This unit is continuously-rated at 320kW at 690–1150rpm, supplying also power for driving the roof-mounted radiator fans and traction motor blowers. Locomotives D1520–74, D1682–1701/7–14 did not have eth fitted, and in their cases the generator group is the Mk IV variant. The auxiliary generator is increased in output to take over the additional loading, being rated at 55kW, 110V, 500A, at 1855rpm. The automatic voltage regulators fitted to the class 47 are as follows: D1500–19, 800V eth generator TG160-16 Mk I Newton-Derby (ND) carbon-pile, 110V auxiliary generator ND carbon-pile self ventilated; D1520–74, D1682–1714, 110V auxiliary generator TG69-28 Mk III ND carbon-pile force ventilated; D1575–1681, D1715–1911, 110V auxiliary generator TG69-20 Mk I or Mk Ia ND carbon-pile force ventilated; and D1912–99, D1100–11, 110V auxiliary generator TG69-20 Mk I or Mk Ia Hawker-Siddeley Dynamics electronic type.

To reduce main generator voltage, burning-out and excessive flashovers at periods of wheel-slip, improve locomotive reliability and reduce maintenance costs, it was decided to change from traction motors connected in series-parallel to all-parallel. This was instigated in 1963, but some time elapsed before it was put into effect. As far as possible standardisation had to be maintained, but a new design of generator had to be fitted. This was Brush type TG172-50 Mk I rated at 4260A, 423V, with a larger commutator, more copper content, but with 12 poles to save weight. Main generator excitation was altered to separate excitation from an inductor type alternator over-hung from the main generator and permanently connected to the separate field-winding through a rectifier. A control winding in the inductor alternator controls the variation of the main excitation current in the separate field circuit. A new load-regulator was fitted. This modification also entailed a new control cubicle, cable layout and other sundry modifications. Locomotives D1575–1681, D1715–1999 and D1100–11 were concerned in this alteration.

The development of the locomotives also resulted in their being fitted with three variations of the Brush type TM64-68 traction motor: Mk I, Ia and Ib. All motors were electrically identical and interchangeable, but Mk I has an armature core fitted on a sleeve which is pressed onto the armature shaft, while the Mk Ia and Ib armature cores are fitted directly onto the armature shaft. The Mk Ib has a bracket provided to carry the WR type aws receiver. Originally the motors were fitted to the following locomotives: Mk I—D1500–49; Mk Ia—D1550 to approximately D1800; Mk Ib—the remainder of the class. Interchangeability has resulted in this arrange-ment changing considerably over the years.

The motors are nose-suspended, axle-hung, with forced-ventilation, having a continuous rating of 368hp, 422V, 710A, at 776rpm. One-hour rating was 362hp, 391V, 762A, at 698rpm. Single-reduction gear with a ratio of 17:66 was fitted. The motors are resiliently suspended from the bogie frame by vertical links and rubber bushes. This allows movement from spring deflections as well as cushioning the gears against starting shock. The centre traction motor on each bogie has a lateral restraining link incor-porating a hydraulic damper. This is fitted between motor carcase and bogie frame to lessen motor wheel and wheel side oscillations. Fitting of the WR type aws to Mk Ib motors involved circuitary modifications and provision of mount-ing brackets so that the aws selector could be fitted. Some ingenuity was required so that accurate distance for operation was maintained between the selector and the mechanical ramp on the track.

The development of the Freightliner concept by BR, and the fact that these trains would be largely hauled by class 47s, made it necessary during 1964 to start fitting air-braking equipment for their operation. An additional motor-driven compressor had to be fitted and the existing one improved. Problems of accommodating new equipment within an already full superstructure were largely overcome by replacement and re-siting. Modifications to the driver's controls and extra pipework to buffer beams for train pipe connections were made. No sooner was this under way than maintenance access problems caused a revision in late 1964, when the Mk II automatic air-brake conversion took over. In this scheme space was created by eliminating the radiator drain tanks and other small items, thereby improving accessibility. To avoid radia-tor freezing at high speeds due to the loss of the drain tanks, hydrostatically-operated radiator intake shutters were installed, locomotives D1631–81 and D1758 upwards being fitted. Drain tanks are provided for engine coolant, which is automatically drained into insulated tanks once the engine shuts down, being returned at engine starting. An additional move was the introduc-tion of a moderate pressure cooling to avoid evaporation losses.

Another operational modification came with the changes in coal train operations to CEGB power stations. Brush developed electronic-control systems to meet the requirements of mgr trains. The ssc allowed a speed of 0·5mph to be maintained while the individual wagons of the mgr train were weighed, loaded or unloaded, and was reliable within close limits. Trials with a semi-manual ssc were not entirely satisfactory because of the excessive interference with the driver's other duties, so a fully automatic system completely out of the drivers' hands was devised. Manual ssc was fitted to D1758–1856/62–1920/77–99 and D1100. In addition D1857–61, D1921–76 and D1101–11 were fully wired throughout, but no speedometers were fitted. The driver set the speed position and selected the speed re-quired, this was then automatically maintained regardless of changes of train load, track or gradient fluctuations. The Brush electronic speed indicator incorporates a multi-toothed wheel with a magnetic pick-up fixed to an axle. This gives a signal at a frequency proportional to the locomotive speed. The signal is fed into an elec-tronic convertor unit which is indicated on dials in the cab. The field-weakening and strengthen-ing of the traction motors is controlled at selected road speed and also at wheel-slip conditions. In 1977 two Knottingley-based class 47s were work-ing with cab-roof flashing lights in connection with their ssc/mgr duties.

Load regulation by electronics is also found on class 47s. This enables diesel engine speed and fuel rack settings to be compared within the governor and fed to the load regulator and so control generator field strength much more quickly than the previous rheostat in generator excitation system.

Electronic equipment was introduced into class 47 from locomotive D1758 from Brush and D1842 from Crewe, the devices being as follows:

(1) Automatic slow speed control
(2) Load regulator
(3) Speed indicating equipment
(4) Traction motor field divert unit
(5) Automatic voltage regulator.

Not all these devices were originally fitted to all locomotives. D1880 was used to test a Sulzer electronic static governor and load regulator. D1703 had a Brush electronic static load regulator.

In the case of D1880 the idea was to provide a locomotive with as near constant horsepower as possible by overcoming the fluctuations of the standard governing system. The hydro-mechanical governor was removed and an electromagnetic actuator fitted to the fuel pump linkage, which in turn was supported by electronics. Modification to the driving controls and traction control equipment gave a wholly electronic control, rather than the pneumatic system which was standard in the class 47. The system generally speeded up and made more sensitive all the operating processes/characteristics of the locomotive, such as rapid engine starting from cold, very sensitive wheelslip detection/correction, constant generator excitation under diesel engine acceleration, together with increased tractive effort, and conversely reduced excitation, protection of turbo-charger from surging. Sulzer claimed greatly simplified maintenance by making use of expendable/exchangeable units, elimination of cleaning, hand fitting, running-in, warming-up, etc.

D1880 was tested before entering service from Sheffield Tinsley depot in early 1966, operating successfully for some five years prior to conversion back to standard when the equipment was considered due for replacement. Other modifications included D1938, modified for remote control for push-and-pull working on a proposed Paddington–Birmingham service, and some eight locomotives experimentally modified to operate at 2200bhp at 700rpm.

For electric train heating, a new Brush dual-wound three-phase alternator was introduced

which also supplied locomotive auxiliaries, so replacing the 110V dc auxiliary generator overhung on the main generator. The train supply was rectified so that the existing two-wire train heating lines could be retained. A nominal 850V is maintained at all engine speeds.

Electrical circuit variations in class 47s resulted in considerable variations, so that at one particular time up to seven different schematics were in use in 512 locomotives. There was much in common in the diagrams, and all were subject to additional modifications to confuse the issue.

The class 47 has had more than its fair share of problems and the most well-known of these were the problems affecting the twin-bank diesel engine. These have been covered in detail elsewhere, but no coverage of this locomotive type can ignore this, so it must be surveyed here. The problems with the twin-bank engine first appeared in the 2500bhp engines fitted in the class 45 and 46 locomotives of BR build. Similar problems with the Mirrlees engines in the Brush type 2 (now class 31) occurred and justified replacement by an EE engine, while the Clayton type 1 suffered an early demise due to its twin-installation of the Paxman 'flat' engine proving almost impossible to maintain. When the difficulties with the class 47 occurred the class was achieving 75 per cent availability—the engine troubles accounting for only 5 per cent of the remaining 15 per cent loss of availability—based on an expected 90 per cent. The engines were repaired or modified during 1966–9, some during casual and others at major overhaul times. A schedule of six per week was soon established, locomotives going to Vickers Ltd at Barrow for engine exchange—a week-long task—one locomotive being exchanged per day. Three-hundred locomotives were dealt with at Barrow, the remainder at BR Crewe works, newest locomotives being done first. At Barrow the engines were exchanged for modified examples using the Vickers-owned old steam locomotive shed at Cavendish Park, which was fitted with an overhead crane.

A locomotive diesel engine has in many cases an arduous and disadvantageous life when compared to engines used in stationary work. The restricted space within a locomotive superstructure makes maintenance difficult, while examination of the engine under full power and load when the locomotive is at work almost impossible. Many of the faults are attributable to vibrations and deflections caused by the interaction of track, locomotive mechanical parts and diesel engine combining to set up stresses which cause malfunctions.

The fact that BR has a disproportionate quantity of locomotives of insufficient power for services which become more arduous year by year, and that the locomotive fleet is aging, is another problem. Many locomotives are driven flat out, others are subject to very variable operation involving periods of high and low outputs.

The twin-bank engine problems began after moderate service time and continued to occur as the engines' ages increased, so that by 1977 the problems were by no means overcome. The faults can be put down to design mistakes, variation in manufacturing quality, maintenance problems, but probably pushing the engine to its power limits is the root cause.

One of the most common problems was the failure of welded areas due to stresses set up by the engine rotational masses and their balancing, causing distortion and vibrations leading to failures. The engine sump under tray fractured and had to be reinforced, the crankcase cross-members or girders failed in their outer legs with fractures, and the crankcase sill plates which fractured at their weld with the A-frames. In this case two semicircular cut-outs were made in the plates, the fractures being visible with the crankcase doors removed. The 12LDA28C engine crankcase is not interchangeable with those of the 'A' and 'B' engines.

The cylinder blocks suffered a number of fractures, and as with the crankcases, the 'C' engine blocks are not interchangeable with those of the 'A' and 'B' engines. In the blocks the sideplate welds developed weak areas and suffered corrosion by coolant water. Re-welding and provision of new plates, plus the introduction of treated coolant to reduce corrosion, has reduced this problem. The cylinder block internal water manifold, which distributes cooling water to the block, developed weld fractures due to poor work and incorrect shaping of the weld. Replacement, or correct procedure overcame this fault. On the cylinder block end casting, poor welding combined with indifferent casting techniques caused fractures. Here the work involved repair or replacement of bad castings by steel plate.

To counteract the out of balance forces set up by the pistons and crankshaft thought responsible for the above, three main changes were carried out on the 12LDA28C engine:

(1) The engine speed was reduced from 800 to 750rpm. (11 per cent reduction in stress)

(2) The angle the twin crankshafts held to each other was increased against each other. This resulted in No 2 crankshaft leading No 1 by $93\frac{1}{2}°$. This was the maximum possible without altering the twin crankshaft timing and synchronising gear. This reduced the vector sum of unbalanced forces from the two crankshafts. (16 per cent reduction in stress)

(3) The mass of the rotating balance weights was increased to give a more suitable balancing ratio. ($12\frac{1}{2}$ per cent reduction in stress)

The total reduction in stress achieved was 36 per cent. The modifications were put into effect from March 1966, and resulted in an effective derating of the locomotives from 2750bhp to 2580bhp, which still applies today. Modifications (2) and (3) were also carried out to engines of 12LDA28B type fitted to classes 45 and 46; modification (1) was not necessary as these engines' rpm was 750. This gave a 27 per cent reduction.

In spite of corrective work between 1969 and 1975, a further 73 class 47 engines had attention for engine sump fractures, and the problem continues. It is solved at Crewe by re-welding, care being taken to avoid heat distortion and costly re-machining. Bolted-on sumps as a replacement were found to be prohibitively costly. In some instances delays in engine modifications can be held responsible for later failures, plus work not properly carried out.

The continual cylinder-head troubles with the twin-bank engine is found in all classes to which it is fitted. Leaking core plugs, almost always the plug adjacent to the exhaust valve housing due to the deterioration of the asbestos washers, caused their replacement by copper rings which proved better. The head castings themselves continue to fracture below the core plug boss, and although repair work is done, the fractures reappear. New stronger heads are fitted in some cases, but cost limitations prevent this in all cases.

Valve stem fractures started in 1976/7. This involves mainly the exhaust valves, and is most serious, due to the broken pieces dropping into the cylinder and damaging the piston crown sufficiently to warrant replacement of piston and cylinder head. If scoring of the cylinder liner occurs, a new one has to be fitted. In some cases broken pieces of the valve find their way into the turbo-charger causing extensive damage and seizing.

Engine crankcase explosions have occurred with the twin-bank units, which have not only resulted in the diesel engine being scrapped, but also considerable damage to the locomotive mechanical parts. High crankcase pressures have resulted in modifications to the engine breathing system, so that from the mid-1960s all models of the engine on BR have had their crankcases fitted with British Internal Combustion Engine Research Association (BICERA) spring-loaded valves, one to each crankcase door.

The cooling radiator systems are almost trouble-free except for burst elements and joints; in contrast to the electrically-powered cooling fans found on classes 44, 45 and the first 20 of class 47, the hydrostatic drive in class 46, and the remaining class 47 to their cooling fans most certainly are not trouble free. The pipe connections require to be very tight to resist the high oil-pressure, and the original steel pipework has been replaced by high-duty reinforced rubber hose which is better. However, the locomotive interior floors continue to feel like 'skating rinks', so leaks and burst hoses still occur. Other leakages required the engine cooling system water to be topped-up frequently, the simple expedient of sticking on the rubber hose and pipe connections having largely reduced topping-up to periods from six months upwards. Water seepage past the rubber sealing rings under the top of the wet-liner was put down to the rubbers being attacked by the anti-corrosion additive in the engine cooling water. New sealing rings and plain liners were fitted. Cylinder liner seals of a new material were tested with success and replaced ones which would only last two-and-a-half years and upset the Sulzer engine maintenance schedules of 10,000 engine hours.

Fuel spillage is the problem of all diesel locomotives; on the class 47 the fitting of non-return valves in the fuel tank balancing pipe solved this and cut down considerably oil contamination of locomotive undergear and traction motors with its attendant fire risks.

Bogie-borne brake equipment caused troubles at around 100,000 miles running when it was found that the rigging was not up to prolonged high-speed running requirements. Too heavy slack adjusters at the bottom of the brake-hangers were partly blamed, as was lateral slackness of the rigging itself. The hangers were stabilised by brackets and wearing plates, and the round-section intermediate tie-bars replaced by box-section units fixed to the hangers and separate pull-rod pins. In late 1963 new slack adjusters were fitted, as well as new brake cylinders and check valves. One-piece brake crank levers were also fitted.

Fracturing of the bogie cast-steel frames caused a programme of ultrasonic examination to be instigated. Some defects were serious, but others only surface defects, but a close watch is still kept on class 47 bogies. In 1975 bogie cross-stretcher fractures began to appear, this necessitating complete replacement or welding repair, according to severity.

Electrical problems included one concerning D1500–19 and their eth generators in which, due to idleness in summer, the commutator was susceptible to glazing and brush-chatter. The result of this was the design of a new double-wound, multi-phase alternator in place of the eth generator and dc auxiliary generator.

The electronic systems for the speedometer, slow-speed engine starting circuits, and others, give continuous problems; while main generators have many problems, including field windings, brush gear failures, bearing failures and overheating. It was reported in early 1976 that up to 100 locomotives per year of class 47 were receiving unclassified repairs for main generator problems, in addition to 150–170 class 47s under classified repairs each year. The long hot summer of 1976 considerably reduced class 47 availability, notably those equipped with eth; again main generators and electronic systems for the load regulators were the principal causes of some regions' percentage availability falling to around 60 per cent.

The WR decided to name 17 of its class 47s, D1660–76 being chosen and provided with nameplates in 1965. Straight cast-aluminium plates with a marked GWR styling were used, varying in length from *Odin* to *Isambard Kingdom Brunel* and *George Jackson Churchward*. The names were, of course, associated with GWR tradition (what else?). As with some other named diesels, nameplates began to disappear in 1973/4 from D1660–76, probably illegally and unofficially. The WR tried to retain all these locomotives, but two spent some years on the ER at Stratford depot, while others are often seen in Scotland and even on the East Coast main line.

The first BR diesel main line locomotive to appear in the rail blue livery was D1733 in May 1964. Apart from the BR double-arrow symbol being on a red panel on the cab sides, the livery was adopted as standard by BR, but did not

Named 47 away from home—47 076 *City of Truro* about to leave platform 4 at Newcastle Central with empty sleeping-cars for Heaton sidings on 4 July 1974. *(Ian S. Carr)*

appear on new class 47s until locomotive D1953 in late 1966. D1733 was so liveried for publicity purposes in association with the XP64 prototype train set, painted in the new rail blue-and-grey livery.

TABLE 14
NAMES OF WR CLASS 47 Co-Co DIESEL-ELECTRICS D1660–D1676 FITTED IN 1965

Number	Name
D1660	City of Truro
D1661	North Star
D1662	Isambard Kingdom Brunel
D1663	Sir Daniel Gooch
D1664	George Jackson Churchward
D1665	Titan
D1666	Odin
D1667	Atlas
D1668	Orion
D1669	Python
D1670	Mammoth
D1671	Thor
D1672	Colossus
D1673	Cyclops
D1674	Samson
D1675	Amazon
D1676	Vulcan

Note: Upon withdrawl of D1671 in 1966 its nameplates were transferred to D1677 in August 1966.

Four class 47s have been involved in accidents which resulted in writing-off and their withdrawal. D1734 was first, being delivered new to the WR in May 1964 only to end its career on 11 January 1965 at Coton Hall, Shrewsbury. It was cut up at Crewe in April. D1671 *Thor* was involved in the double collision near Bridgend on 19 December 1965 when, hauling an empty carriage train to Bristol, it ran into a landslip and was derailed, being then almost immediately hit by class 37 D6983 with an empty wagon train heading for Margam. Both locomotives were scrapped, D1671 being withdrawn in August 1966 and cut-up by R. S. Hayes Ltd, Bridgend. Its nameplates were transferred to D1677 the same month. D1908 was severely damaged on 8 April 1969 at Monmore Green, Wolverhampton, being withdrawn during August and cut-up at Crewe in October. Fire damage removed D1562 at Haughley on the GE section. It was cut-up at Crewe in October 1971.

Perhaps the most spectacular and costly accident was that involving D1617 on the 02.25 Birkenhead–Etruria iron-ore train, which ran out of control approaching Chester and was diverted into the diesel depot to avoid the station. D1617 and its train effectively demolished a number of class 24 Sulzers, of which four were so badly damaged as to be scrapped. This happened on 9 July 1969. D1617, in spite of severe damage, was repaired at Crewe. The derailment of 47 046 (D1628) at Peterborough on 29 September 1974 resulted not in withdrawal but in a complete rebuilding with a new superstructure at Crewe works, to form an uprated class 47 incorporating a new Brush main and auxiliary alternator set plus a range of automatic and electronic control gear. As 47 601 it is powered by an EE/GEC 16CSVTIII 3250bhp engine, and classified 47/6, but its re-powering with a non-Sulzer engine lifts it out of our coverage here.

The first class 47 was completed at the Loughborough works of Brush Traction Ltd in the late summer of 1962. Numbered D1500, it was very effectively liveried in a two-tone BR green scheme involving broad horizontal bands carried completely round the locomotive, except for the yellow warning panel on each cab front. D1500 was weighed at Crewe during September, then sent back to Loughborough, arriving next at Finsbury Park depot on the ER later that month. All 20 of the first batch were based there for East Coast main line mixed-traffic duties. Following crew training and runs on Cambridge and Hull duties from King's Cross, D1500 was involved in

In its original two-tone green livery, class 47 D1502 climbs lustily through Holbeck High Level closed station from Leeds Central with the up 'Yorkshire Pullman' on 20 July 1963.   *(Brian Webb)*

test runs with a dynamometer car between King's Cross and Doncaster. On 11 October, D1500 took a 385-ton train on this route, departing King's Cross at 10.12 and arriving Doncaster 12.31; it returned south at 13.22.

Following the delivery of D1501 to Finsbury Park in November, D1500 was lent to the WR where it did further dynamometer car trials from Swindon Experimental Unit on Paddington–Cheltenham trains, and to Plymouth, returning again in 1963. The results of Swindon tests were that under controlled road conditions the class 47 was capable of a maximum rail tractive effort of 71,700lb at 6·5mph, equalling 28·1 per cent of the locomotive's weight, this being before engine derating. Rail hp was maintained constant at 2250 between train speeds of 30 and 80mph—the generator unloading point. Efficiency between generator input and output at the rail varied from $83\frac{1}{2}$ to $84\frac{1}{2}$ per cent between 30 and 80mph. Fuel consumption at maximum power was 1025lb/hr.

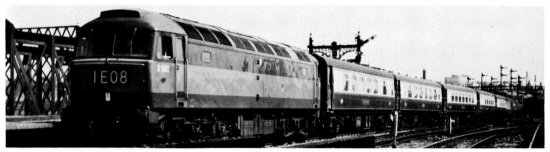

Locomotives up to D1507 were delivered by the end of January 1963, and crew training was under way at Gateshead, being soon followed by training at Leeds (Neville Hill), Sheffield (Darnall) and Edinburgh (Haymarket) depots. The locomotives soon made themselves at home on East Coast main line freights, coal trains and on King's Cross–Millerhill fitted freights. In March and May the 'Tees-Tyne Pullman', 'Flying Scotsman' and 'The Master Cutler' were often class 47 powered, and by summer, in association with the EE Deltics and class 46, had ousted the class 40 from most important duties.

Freight tests on the Doncaster–Grimsby line demonstrated that a class 47 could start a 1500-ton iron-ore train on a 1 in 93 gradient at Appleby, during which feat the dynamometer car registered a drawbar tractive effort of 66,500lb, representing almost 70,000lb at the wheels. On these tests the anti-slip brake was applied to simulate poor adhesion conditions. Other early

trials involved taking a 637-ton load of coaching stock up the 1 in 37·7 Lickey incline, giving a tractive effort of 64,300lb.

The first of the production batch of 47s from Brush, D1520–49, were allocated to Darnall from June 1963, not being based at Tinsley until that depot opened in April 1964. They were mostly employed on freight traffic, taking on the class 7 freights between Shirebrook and New England, Whitemoor and Doncaster. During October 1963, D1500 was tested on the LMR West Coast main line from Crewe to Carlisle, and to Shrewsbury.

Progress on the railway workshop licence-built class 47s at Crewe was slow, for although work was under way on D1550–69 for the ER in the spring of 1963, it was not until the following January that the first locomotive reached Darnall. An interesting point about the Crewe-built diesel locomotives is that in 1965 BR issued comparative construction costs figures for the Crewe-

Above: A load of high-capacity bogie oil-tankers forms the Teesport–Jarrow train headed by class 47 D1769 as it passes just north of Chester le Street on 6 August 1969. *(Ian S. Carr)*

Below: The 1977 Silver Jubilee celebrations caused the ER at Stratford to deck out two of its class 47s with the Union Jack. 47 163 is seen at Stratford depot on 9 July 1977. *(John A. Howie)*

built class 52 diesel-hydraulic of 2700hp which were put at £135,000, or £10,000 more than the class 47s built there. By this time Brush was building its batch starting at D1682 for the WR, but from this point deliveries are so complex as to require separate regional coverage, and this has been adopted.

The ER went on to take D1758–D1806/62–1900 in 1964/5 from Brush, Sheffield receiving the lion's share, with a few to Immingham. By this time the NER had gotten D1570–82 from Crewe, four going to Holbeck and nine to Gateshead in March–May 1964. In 1965–7, D1977–99 and D1100–11 went to the NER at Gateshead and York depots. Their widespread use saw them render the King's Cross A4 Pacifics redundant in the autumn of 1963; these were transferred to less arduous duties north of the Border. The class

47s proved themselves able to handle some Deltic diagrams, a task they still perform when the 3300bhp locomotives are not available. In early 1965 the GE section put class 47s on its main Liverpool Street–Norwich and Lowestoft line trains, some excellent running being accomplished. During the early winter of 1968, Gateshead and SR locomotives from Eastleigh alternated on Freightliners on Newcastle–Southampton services; this interesting duty lasted until late spring 1969. During this time Eastleigh locomotives found their way to Edinburgh on filling-in turns. A late 1969 proposal to move D1500–19 with eth to the LMR was preceded by trials with D1518/9, but the idea lapsed, and the majority of this batch remain at Finsbury Park. At the time of writing in 1977 these locomotives, the oldest of the class, continue to handle some of the

Above: An Anglo-Scottish Freightliner heads south-
wards past the rear of Newcastle Central with class 47
47 494 on 15 July 1977.   *(Ian S. Carr)*

Below: Named 47 on its home ground—47 077 *North Star* at West Ealing on the WR with the 08.21 Parkeston–Oxford South Freightliner on 22 February 1975.   *(Norman E. Preedy)*

Above: Almost new, and one of the first turned out in the then new rail blue livery, class 47 D1958 takes a freight through Carlisle on the goods lines near Rome Street on a dull 9 February 1967.   *(Brian Webb)*

fastest locomotive-hauled trains on BR in spite of their 14 years' hard work. In late 1975 an unusual duty for 47 155 (D1748) was its use at the non-rail served Thamesside power station at West Thurrock as a temporary generator exciter.

The WR received D1682–1701/7–57 batch from Brush in 1963/4, the first two locomotives being weighed at Derby in October 1963. Although a handful went to the LMR at Kirkby shed for coal train traffic, the batch was soon delivered at three to four locomotives each week, so that Derby works finish-painted some loco-motives from Brush, resulting in some loss of sequence between locomotive running numbers and Brush maker's numbers. On the WR they soon were at work out of Paddington to Wolver-hampton and Birmingham. Based at Old Oak Common initially, training was soon in progress at Cardiff (Canton) and Swansea (Landore), which received allocations in 1964/5. D1583–D1615 were built at Crewe for the WR in 1964, and 1965 produced D1636–81, D1962–7 from there, and D1901–38 from Brush in 1965/6.

Through workings, such as Swansea–Crewe–Carlisle freights and Milford Haven–Thornton (Fife) block oil trains, took WR locomotives to Carlisle in 1965, and to the ER on Bristol (Severn Beach)–Immingham freights. Mid-1966 found WR class 47s on R. T. B. Spencer Works iron-ore trains to and from Newport (Mon.), and on Paddington–West of England expresses due to a spate of disel-hydraulic locomotive troubles. Until the advent of the High Speed Trains (HST), the class 47s shared with the class 50 and the last class 52 diesel-hydraulics all the WR top duties, and are still hard at work with the class 50s on West of England duties.

The Southern and Scottish regions have only had small allocations of class 47 locomotives, although they are no strangers to their territories. The SR only had six ex-WR locomotives, D1921–6, allocated to Eastleigh depot during 1966–8. They worked all types of duties, including the Southampton, Bournemouth and Weymouth

Royal train duty is the task of immaculate class 47 No 47 172 at Scarborough on 2 July 1975 when HM The Queen and the Duke of Edinburgh visited Duchy of Lancaster estates in the area.   *(J. Robin Lidster)*

expresses, and boat trains. They were replaced by the class 74 2300/650bhp electro-diesel locomotive rebuilds, and the six returned to the WR. The Scottish Region received D1968–76 new from Crewe in late 1965 and based them all at Haymarket. Subsequently the region acquired others by inter-regional transfer, so that Glasgow (Eastfield) also now has an allocation of the class. A wide useage is found for the Scottish-based locomotives, which not only took on Anglo-Scottish duties, but, with visiting class 47s, worked into the north of Scotland. From mid-1968 the region's own locomotives were taking on Edinburgh–Aberdeen and Glasgow–Aberdeen trains. Electrification of the West Coast main line cut down their appearances on that route, but the G & SWR route via Kilmarnock and Dumfries is still their regular haunt, notably in summer when the normal diesel multiple-unit services are replaced by locomotive-hauled trains.

The LMR received D1616–35 and D1842–61 from Crewe in 1964/5, which went to Toton and Crewe North depots, and D1807–41 and D1939–61 from Brush in 1965/6. The last two locomotives, D1960/1, were not taken into stock until July 1967 and May 1968 respectively for, being electronic testbeds for various systems then being applied piecemeal to the class, they spent some time at the Technical and Research Centre at Derby. Allocations to the Midland line and Crewe North (Western lines) saw them sweep

Left: Amid the tangle of electrification, class 47 No D1828 heads an ingots train past Gretna Junction in 1973.

(Peter W. Robinson)

Below: Under the wires and the shadows of the city walls, class 47 47 534 enters Carlisle with a Glasgow–Carlisle G & SW line stopping train at 14.50 on 9 July 1977.

(Brian Webb)

steam from Nottinghamshire, but the West Coast main line was slow to draft them on to its top passenger work. Apart from the Freightliners, always class 47 worked, the 'Royal Highlander', with its Crewe–Perth/Perth–Glasgow/ Glasgow–Aberdeen (as far as Perth)/Perth–Crewe diagram, was worked by the class from early 1965. By May 1965 their use on the West Coast main line expresses increased, and the 'Mid-Day Scot' and various Euston-Perth, Birmingham–Edinburgh and Liverpool–Glasgow trains were taken over from the class 40s, though the latter were still common. From January 1966 'The Royal Scot' was worked by class 47s. Their use was short-lived, for the introduction of the EE-built class 50 2700bhp Co-Co diesel-electrics in 1968/9 saw them completely eclipsed, apart from the Birmingham and Manchester–Glasgow services.

An interesting aspect of class 47 freight haulage was that during 1972/3 the locomotives were hauling coal trains composed of 55 BR 32-ton hoppers with a 1650-ton payload and gross train weight of 2341 tons between NCB Newstead

Colliery and the CEGB Staythorpe Power Station in the Nottingham Division. Bearing in mind the ballyhoo made in 1968 when the 4000bhp Brush *Kestrel* hauled 2028 tons and claimed this as a record. The class 47, even in its derated 2580bhp form, is not doing so badly.

In mid-1977 the class 47 was still causing some concern, and the eth-fitted locomotives in particular on the LMR were steadily drifting downwards in availability. On the ER a spate of control-gear failures had set in, while on the WR fracturing of some traction motor interpoles was occurring.

The five-year refurbishing programme for class 47 started in 1976 to prolong their life and increase availability has produced some improvement. The programme includes work on the electrical equipment, such as re-insulation of field coils, the armature being vacuum impregnated, and the replacement of steel bandings with glass tape, and on the main generator, armature rewinding, fitting of new commutators and new insulation. The traction motors were overhauled and flash tested. Work on the diesel engines is in line with operating experience as previously mentioned. The cost of this programme is said to be 10 per cent of that of building new locomotives.

Five of the class 47s were put aside for trials with a batch of the Sulzer Vee-type engine in its 12-cylinder form. Subsequently locomotives D1702–6, built by Brush, appeared equipped with the 12LVA24 engine rated at 2650bhp at 1050rpm. Putting out 100bhp less than the twin-bank powered locomotives, D1702–6, or class 48 as they were known, had similar traction characteristics, retaining the same electrical equipment,

A Cuban 47! One of ten 12LVA24 engined 2580bhp Co-Co locomotives built at Loughborough in 1965 for the Clayton Equipment Co. Ltd to meet an urgent order from Cuban National Railways. As originally delivered these locomotives were in BR two-tone green livery.   *(Clayton Equipment Co. Ltd)*

albeit in modified form. Some re-design of interior layout was necessary, but the low height of the 12LVA24 was very noticeable in the engine compartment.

The Brush main generator was a variation of type TG160-60 Mk IV, in fact the Mk V version. Changes were necessary due to the clockwise rotation of the engine (the twin-bank synchronising gear driving the class 47 generators anti-clockwise) and lower engine rpm of 1050 instead of 1150; in addition the self-field was stronger to maintain a voltage similar to standard. D1703 was fitted with a static load-regulator.

Plans to allocate the locomotives to Finsbury Park depot were changed and delivery to the ER, so far as dates into traffic were concerned, occupied the period September 1965–July 1966; officially allocated to Tinsley, they were in fact outstationed at Shirebrook depot for freight working, followed by the possibility of Sheffield–King's Cross expresses. Re-allocations took D1703–6 to Norwich depot, and then Stratford in 1969, where they worked GE line freight and passenger duties, finally returning to Tinsley in early 1970. By late 1967 the locomotives had run for 8000 to 9000 hours and accumulated over 115,000 miles in traffic.

They were never popular with BR, but this was probably due more to being non-standard than to shortcomings, although bearing problems occurred with the engines. A decision to convert them to class 47 was made, and 1969 saw them on their last GE section duties from Stratford depot, where their reliability was not good. In April 1969, D1702 had been at Crewe works for nine months awaiting a decision on conversion. It was finally outshopped as a class 47 during December, by which time the remainder had also got to Crewe. Conversion was a slow process, their official change of classification being: D1702, 12/69; D1703, 11/70; D1704, 6/71; D1705, 4/71; D1706, 11/70. The engines were reputedly sold to a dealer, but later returned to Sulzer and were

shipped to France for use on locomotives there.

An unusual outcome of the class 47/48 occurred in 1963, when the Cuban National Railways, somewhat short of motive power due to Dr Castro's estrangement from the USA, and hence spares for his country's diesel locomotives, sought a suitable off-the-shelf design for quick purchase. The result was a batch of ten BR class 47s adapted to suit Cuban requirements. Due to political overtones, the contract was not made public until late 1965, by which time most of the batch had been delivered. For the same reason the locomotives were 'officially' built and supplied by the Clayton Equipment Co. Ltd, of Tutbury, Derby, and carried Clayton works plates. The locomotives were in fact built by

Brush at Loughborough, alongside current BR production. The locomotives were fitted with the Sulzer 12LVA24 vee-engine rated at 2534bhp at 1050rpm and had Brush electrical equipment. The design was modified to take centre buffer/drawgear units, the cab roof to take a powerful headlight, the cooling gear to suit tropical conditions, and illuminated locomotive number boxes were fixed to front cab sides. Only air-braking was fitted. The locomotives were even finished in BR two-tone green livery and numbered 2501–10. In Cuba they were later repainted. At the time of their shipment, these locomotives were the most powerful diesels exported from the UK. Subsequently, Brush delivered under its own name a quantity of lightweight diesel-electrics to Cuba.

TABLE 16
BR CLASS 47 AND 48 Co-Co DIESEL-ELECTRIC LOCOMOTIVES
SHOWING MAIN CLASS VARIATIONS AT 1966/7 PERIOD

Data	Brush built locomotives	BR Crewe built locomotives	Variation
	D1500–49 D1682–1841 D1862–1961	D1550–1681 D1842–61 D1962–99 D1100–11	
Tractive effort:			
Maximum	D1500–19		55,000lb/12·7mph
Continuous	D1500–19		30,000lb/27mph
Maximum	D1702–6		62,000lb/10·25mph
Continuous	D1702–6		30,000lb/26mph
Maximum	Remainder	Remainder	62,000lb/10·5mph
Continuous	Remainder	Remainder	30,000lb/27mph
Brake system	D1500–19		Westinghouse AV/D air
	D1520–49 D1682–1757	D1550–1630	Metcalfe-Oerlikon AV/D air
	D1758–1841 D1862–1961	D1631–81 D1842–61 D1962–99 D1100–11	Metcalfe-Oerlikon Dual/D air
Boiler (steam train-heating)	D1500–49 D1682–1781	D1550–1615	Spanner Mk III
		D1616–30	Stone-Vapor
	D1837–41 D1862–74 D1948–61	D1631–8 D1842–61 D1962–76 D1101–11	Universal boiler compartment. Stone-Vapor fitted
		D1639–81 D1901–47 D1977–99 D1100	Universal boiler compartment. Clayton Mk II fitted.
	D1782–1836 D1875–1900		Universal boiler compartment. None fitted. 35cwt ballast carried

Boiler power supply	D1500–49 D1682–1757	D1550–1630	From batteries
	D1758–1841 D1862–1961	D1631–81 D1842–61 D1962–99 D1100–11	From auxiliary generator
Generator excitation with series-parallel traction motor connection	D1500–49 D1682–1714	D1550–74	Self, separate, series — Direct from auxiliary generator. Combined decompounding and starting
Generator excitation with all parallel traction motor connection	D1715–1841 D1862–1961	D1575–1681 D1842–61 D1962–99 D1100–11	Self, separate, series — From inductor alternator exciter after rectification. Decompounding separate starting winding
Main generator type	D1500–19		TG160-60 Mk II
	D1520–49 D1682–1701 D1707–14	D1550–74	TG160-60 Mk IV
	D1702–6		TG160-60 Mk V
	D1715–1841 D1862–1961	D1575–1681 D1842–61 D1962–99 D1100–11	TG172-50 Mk I
Auxiliary generator type	D1500–19		TG69-16 Mk I
	D1520–49 D1682–1701 D1707–14	D1550–74	TG69-24 Mk III
	D1715–1841 D1862–1961	D1575–1681 D1842–61 D1962–99 D1100–11	TG69-20 Mk I or Mk IA
	D1702–6		TG69-28 Mk III
Eth generator	D1500–19		TG160-16 Mk I
Traction motor blower motors	D1500–19		TAM28-20 Mk II
	Remainder	Remainder	TAM28-16 Mk V
Vacuum exhauster motor	D1500–49 D1682–1706	D1550–82	TAM28-12 Mk II
	Remainder	Remainder	TAM28-16 Mk VI
Air compressor motor	D1500–19		Westinghouse
	D1520–49 D1682–1706	D1550–1630	TAM28-12 Mk III
	D1707–1841 D1862–1961	D1631–81 D1842–61 D1962–99 D1100–11	TAM28-12 Mk IIIA (two motors)
Radiator fan motor (electric)	D1500–19		VAM42-16 Mk II Remainder Serck-Behr hydrostatic fan drive
Slow-speed control and electronic speed indication	D1758–1841 D1862–1961	D1842–61 D1962–99 D1100–11	
Traction motor suspension tubes	D1500–19		Timken and Hoffmann (ten locomotives with each)
	D1520–49		Hoffmann
	D1682–1841 D1862–1961	D1550–1681 D1842–61 D1962–99 D1100–11	Hoffmann split tubes (except for 110 locomotives in D1862–1999/D1100–11 series with SKF suspension units)

TABLE 17   MAIN VARIATIONS IN CLASS 47 Co-Co DIESEL-ELECTRICS BASED ON BRITISH RAIL DIAGRAM BOOK MT25 OF 1974

Class	47/0	47/0	47/0	47/0	47/0	47/0	47/0	47/0
Diagram number	47aX	47bX	47cV	47dX	47eX	47fX	47gX	47hX
Weight in working order	118t 14c	118t 13c	114t 7c	117t 19c	118t 10c	115t 7c	117t 5c	116t 19c
Fuel capacity, gal	765	765	765	765	765	765	765	765
Boiler water capacity, gal	1250	1250	1250	1250	1200	1200	1200	1200
Generator type	BT TG172 -50 Mk I	BT TG160 -60 Mk II	TG160-60 Mk IV	TG160-60 Mk IV	TG172-50 Mk I	TG172-50 Mk I	TG172-50 Mk I	TG172-50 Mk I
Traction motor type	TM64-68 1A	TM64-68 1	TM64-68 1A	TM64-68 1A	TM64-68 1A	TM64-68 1A	TM64-68 1A	TM64-68 1A
Rail hp at maximum rating[1]	2160	2160	2160	2160	2160	2160	2160	2160
Maximum tractive effort, lb	62,000	62,000	62,000	62,000	62,000	62,000	62,000	62,000
Continuous tractive effort, lb/27mph	30,000	30,000	30,000	30,000	30,000	30,000	30,000	30,000
Train heating — Boiler type	Spanner Mk III	Spanner Mk III	Spanner Mk III	Spanner Mk III	Spanner Mk III	Vapor OK4625	Vapor OK4625	Clayton Mk II
Train heating — Electric	—	—	—	—	—	—	—	—
Braking — Locomotive	SA AA AA ACV	SA AA AA ACV	A V	SA AA AA ACV	SA AA AA ACV	A V	SA AA AA ACV	SA AA AA ACV

Notes: [1] When derated to 2580bhp the rail hp is 2080.
　　　Owing to complex renumbering adopted for class 47 these will be found on table number 19.
　　　Some of these diagrams are now obsolete due to continuation of dual braking/eth fitting programmes.

**TABLE 15
VARIATIONS IN ELECTRICAL EQUIPMENT
USED IN PRODUCTION CLASS 47 LOCOMOTIVES
D1520–D1999/D1100–11 AT AUGUST 1965**

Locomotives	Motor con-nec-tions	Start-ing con-tactors	Field divert	Speed control	Train brakes	Notes
D1520–74	SP	EP	R	N	V	
D1575–1630	AP	EP	R	N	V	
D1631–81	AP	EP	R	N	D	
D1682–1714	SP	EP	R	N	V	1, 2
D1715–57	AP	EP	R	N	V	
D1758–1841	AP	EP	R	SS	D	
D1842–56	AP	EM	R	SS	D	
D1857–61	AP	EM	R	N	D	
D1862–1920	AP	EM	S	SS	D	3, 4, 5
D1921–76	AP	EM	S	N	D	5, 6
D1977–99	AP	EM	S	SS	D	6
D1100	AP	EM	S	SS	D	6
D1101–11	AP	EM	S	N	D	6

Abbreviations: SP—motors connected in series-parallel
　　　　　　　AP—motors connected in all-parallel
　　　　　　　EP—electro-pneumatic
　　　　　　　EM—electro-magnetic
　　　　　　　R—relays
　　　　　　　S—static
　　　　　　　N—normal
　　　　　　　SS—slow speed
　　　　　　　V—vacuum
　　　　　　　D—dual

Notes: 1—D1702–6 have Vee engines
　　　　2—D1703 has static load-regulator
　　　　3—D1880 has static governor and load regulator
　　　　4—D1894–7 have automatic SS control
　　　　5—D1913–51 have static AVRs
　　　　6—D1962–D1111 have static AVRs

47/0	47/0	47/3	47/4	47/4	47/4	47/4	47/4	47/4	47/4	47/4
47jX	47kV	47/3aX	47/4aX	47/4bX	47/4cX	47/4dX	47/4eX	47/4fX	47/4gX	47/4hX
114t 9c	115t 5c	111t 18c	119t 9c	120t 14c	118t 9c	119t 19c	119t 1c	121t 12c	123t 4c	120t 11c
765	765	765	765	765	765	765	765	765	765	765
1250	1200	—	1250	1250	1250	1250	1250	1250	1200	1200
TG160-60 Mk II	TG172-50 Mk I	TG172-50 Mk I	TG160-60	TG160-60 Mk II	TG160-60 Mk II	TG160-6 Mk IV	TG160-6 Mk IV	TG172-50 Mk I	TG172-50 Mk I	TG172-50 Mk I
TM64-68 1	TM64-68 1A	TM64-68 1A	TM64-68	TM64-68 1	TM64-68 1	TM64-68 1A	TM64-68 1A	TM64-68 1	TM64-68 1A	TM64-68 1A
2160	2160	2160	2160	2160	2160	2160	2160	2160	2160	2160
62,000	62,000	62,000	55,000	62,000	62,000	62,000	62,000	62,000	62,000	62,000
30,000	30,000	30,000	30,000	30,000	30,000	30,000	30,000	30,000	30,000	30,000
Spanner Mk III	Spanner Mk III	—	Spanner Mk III	Spanner Mk III	—	Spanner Mk III	—	Spanner Mk III	Vapor OK4625	—
—	—	—	TG160-16	BL100-30	BL100-30	BL100-30	BL100-30	BL100-30	BL100-30	BL100-30
A	A	SA AA	SA AA	SA AA	SA AA	SA AA	SA AA	SA AA	SA AA	SA AA
V	V	AA ACV	AA ACV	AA ACV	AA ACV	AA ACV	AA ACV	AA ACV	AA ACV	AA ACV

TABLE 18
BUILDING WORKS, MAKERS' NUMBERS AND DATES INTO RUNNING STOCK FOR CLASS 47 AND 48 Co-Co DIESEL-ELECTRIC LOCOMOTIVES

No.	Builder	Works No.	Date	Region
D1500–2	Brush	342–4	11/62	E
D1503	Brush	345	12/62	E
D1504–8	Brush	346–50	1/63	E
D1509–11	Brush	351–3	2/63	E
D1512–5	Brush	354/5/7/6	3/63	E
D1516–7	Brush	358/9	4/63	E
D1518	Brush	413	5/63	E
D1519	Brush	360	4/63	E
D1520–9	Brush	414/5/7/6/9/8/20–3	6/63	E
D1530–2	Brush	424–6	7/63	E
D1533–7	Brush	427–31	8/63	E
D1538–43	Brush	432–4/6/5/8	9/63	E
D1544–9	Brush	437/9/40–3	10/63	E
D1550–4	Crewe		1/64	E
D1555–8	Crewe		2/64	E
D1559–62	Crewe		3/64	E
D1563	Crewe		4/64	E
D1564–9	Crewe		3/64	E
D1570	Crewe		3/64	NE
D1571–7	Crewe		4/64	NE
D1578–82	Crewe		5/64	NE
D1583–90	Crewe		5/64	W
D1591–1600	Crewe		6/64	W
D1601–8	Crewe		7/64	W
D1609–15	Crewe		8/64	W
D1616–8	Crewe		P 9/64	LM
D1619–23	Crewe		P10/64	LM
D1624	Crewe		P11/64	LM
D1625	Crewe		P10/64	LM
D1626–31	Crewe		P11/64	LM
D1632–5	Crewe		P12/64	LM
D1636–46	Crewe		12/64	W
D1647–55	Crewe		1/65	W
D1656–64	Crewe		2/65	W
D1665–72	Crewe		3/65	W
D1673–8	Crewe		4/65	W
D1679–81	Crewe		5/65	W
D1682/3	Brush	444/5	10/63	W
D1684–92	Brush	446–54	11/63	W
D1693–7	Brush	455–8/60	12/63	W
D1698	Brush	459	1/64	W
D1699	Brush	461	12/63	W
D1700/1	Brush	462/3	1/64	W
D1702	Brush	464	11/65	E
D1703	Brush	465	9/65	E
D1704	Brush	466	7/66	E
D1705	Brush	467	11/65	E
D1706	Brush	468	12/65	E
D1707–13	Brush	469–75	1/64	W
D1714–9	Brush	476/7/87–90	2/64	W
D1720–6	Brush	491–7	3/64	W
D1727–30	Brush	498–501	4/64	W
D1731	Brush	502	6/64	W
D1732	Brush	503	4/64	W
D1733	Brush	504	6/64	W
D1734/5	Brush	505/6	5/64	W
D1736	Brush	508	4/64	W
D1737/8	Brush	507/9	5/64	W
D1739–41	Brush	510–2	6/64	W
D1742	Brush	513	5/64	W

No.	Builder	Works No.	Date	Region	No.	Builder	Works No.	Date	Region
D1743/4	Brush	514/5	6/64	W	D1903–5	Brush	665–7	9/65	W
D1745–8	Brush	516–9	7/64	W	D1906	Brush	668	10/65	W
D1749–53	Brush	486/78–81	7/64	W	D1907	Brush	669	9/65	W
D1754/5	Brush	482/3	8/64	W	D1908–13	Brush	670–5	10/65	W
D1756/7	Brush	484/5	9/64	W					
D1758	Brush	520	5/64	E	D1914	Brush	676	11/65	W
D1759	Brush	521	8/64	E	D1915	Brush	677	12/65	W
D1760–6	Brush	522–8	9/64	E	D1916	Brush	678	11/65	W
D1767–72	Brush	529–34	10/64	E	D1917	Brush	679	12/65	W
D1773	Brush	535	9/65	E	D1918–20	Brush	680–2	11/65	W
D1774–6	Brush	536–8	10/64	E	D1921–5	Brush	683–7	12/65	W
D1777	Brush	539	11/64	E					
					D1926–8	Brush	688–90	1/66	W
D1778–80	Brush	540–2	10/64	E	D1929–32	Brush	691–4	2/66	W
D1781–4	Brush	543–6	11/64	E	D1933–6	Brush	695–8	3/66	W
D1785	Brush	547	12/64	E	D1937/8	Brush	699/700	4/66	W
D1786/7	Brush	548/9	11/64	E	D1939	Brush	701	P 4/66	LM
D1788	Brush	550	12/64	E	D1940	Brush	702	P 6/66	LM
D1789	Brush	551	11/64	E	D1941	Brush	703	P 7/66	LM
					D1942	Brush	704	P 6/66	LM
D1790/1	Brush	552/3	12/64	E	D1943–7	Brush	705–9	P 7/66	LM
D1792	Brush	554	1/65	E	D1948	Brush	610	P 8/66	LM
D1793/4	Brush	555/6	12/64	E	D1949/50	Brush	611/2	P 9/66	LM
D1795–1803	Brush	557–65	1/65	E	D1951/2	Brush	613/4	P11/66	LM
D1804	Brush	566	2/65	E					
D1805/6	Brush	567/8	1/65	E	D1953–5	Brush	615–7	P12/66	LM
					D1956	Brush	618	P13/66	LM
D1807–9	Brush	569–71	P 1/65	M	D1957	Brush	619	P 1/67	LM
D1810–6	Brush	572–8	P 2/65	M	D1958/9	Brush	620/1	P 2/67	LM
D1817	Brush	579	P 3/65	M	D1960	Brush	622	7/67	LM
D1818–20	Brush	580–2	P 2/65	M	D1961	Brush	623	5/68	LM
D1821–30	Brush	583–92	P 3/65	M					
D1831	Brush	593	P 5/65	M	D1962–4	Crewe		9/65	W
					D1965–7	Crewe		10/65	W
D1832	Brush	594	P 4/65	M	D1968–72	Crewe		P11/65	Sc
D1833	Brush	595	P 5/65	M	D1973–6	Crewe		P12/65	Sc
D1834	Brush	596	P 4/65	M	D1977–83	Crewe		12/65	NE
D1835	Brush	597	P 5/65	M	D1984–7	Crewe		1/66	NE
D1836	Brush	598	P 4/65	M					
D1837–9	Brush	599–601	P 5/65	M	D1988–90	Crewe		2/66	NE
					D1991–3	Crewe		3/66	NE
D1840	Brush	602	P 6/65	M	D1994/5	Crewe		4/66	NE
D1841	Brush	603	P 5/65	M	D1996	Crewe		5/66	NE
D1842–4	Crewe		P 5/65	M	D1997–9	Crewe		6/66	NE
D1845–51	Crewe		P 6/65	M	D1100	Crewe		7/66	NE
D1852–4	Crewe		P 7/65	M					
D1855–8	Crewe		P 8/65	M	D1101	Crewe		8/66	NE
					D1102	Crewe		9/66	NE
D1859–61	Crewe		P 9/65	M	D1103/4	Crewe		10/66	NE
D1862–8	Brush	624–30	5/65	E	D1105/6	Crewe		11/66	NE
D1869–72	Brush	631–4	6/65	E	D1107	Crewe		12/66	NE
D1873	Brush	635	5/65	E	D1108/10	Crewe		1/67	NE
D1874	Brush	636	6/65	E					
D1875	Brush	637	7/65	E	D1111	Crewe		2/67	NE
D1876–8	Brush	638–40	6/65	E					
D1879	Brush	641	7/65	E					
D1880	Brush	642	2/66	E					
D1881	Brush	643	6/65	E					
D1882–5	Brush	644–7	7/65	E					
D1886/7	Brush	648/9	8/65	E					
D1888–90	Brush	650–2	7/65	E					
D1891–3	Brush	653–5	8/65	E					
D1894	Brush	656	12/65	E					
D1895–7	Brush	657–9	9/65	E					
D1898/9	Brush	660/1	8/65	E					
D1900	Brush	662	9/65	E					
D1901	Brush	663	9/65	W					
D1902	Brush	664	10/65	W					

Note: Due to the lack of surviving information on the allocation of Brush works numbers, the above list is as accurate as possible at the time of going to press, although all the data cannot be guaranteed.

TABLE 19
RENUMBERING OF BRUSH- AND CREWE-BUILT
Co-Co DIESEL-ELECTRICS OF CLASSES 47 AND 48

Original No.	Renumbering	Original No.	Renumbering	Original No.	Renumbering
D1500–20	47 401–21	D1656	47 072	D1950	47 552
D1521–4	47 001–4	D1657	47 537	D1951–5	47 507–11
D1525	47 422			D1956/7	47 553/4
D1526	47 005	D1658–61	47 074–7	D1958–61	47 512–5
D1527	47 423	D1662	47 484	D1962–7	47 262–7
D1528–30	47 006–8	D1663–8	47 078–83		
		D1669	47 538	D1968	47 516
D1531	47 424	D1670	47 085	D1969–74	47 268–73
D1532	47 009	D1671	withdrawn	D1975	47 517
D1533–6	47 425–8			D1976–99	47 274–97
D1537–40	47 010–3	D1672	47 086	D1100	47 298
D1541/2	47 429/30	D1673–7	47 087–91	D1101–11	47 518–28
D1543/4	47 014/5	D1678	47 534		
		D1679–82	47 093–6	Locomotives shown as withdrawn were not allocated new numbers.	
D1545	47 431	D1683	47 485		
D1546	47 016	D1684	47 097		
D1547–50	47 432–5				
D1551	47 529	D1685–8	47 098–101		
D1552–61	47 436–45	D1689	47 486	**TABLE 20**	
D1562	withdrawn	D1690–1706	47 102–18	**THE SECOND RENUMBERING OF THE**	
		D1707	47 487	**CLASS 47 LOCOMOTIVE**	
D1563–9	47 446–52	D1708–12	47 119–23		
D1570	47 017	D1713	47 488		

Original No.	Intermediate No.	Final No.
D1584	47 021	47 531
D1585	47 022	47 542
D1588	47 023	47 543
D1592	47 025	47 544
D1641	47 057	47 532
D1642	47 058	47 547
D1646	47 062	47 545
D1649	47 065	47 535
D1651	47 067	47 533
D1655	47 071	47 536
D1657	47 073	47 537
D1669	47 084	47 538
D1678	47 092	47 534
D1715	47 125	47 548
D1717	47 126	47 555
D1718	47 127	47 529
D1723	47 132	47 540
D1724	47 133	47 549
D1731	47 139	47 550
D1746	47 153	47 551
D1747	47 154	47 546
D1755	47 161	47 541
D1930	47 253	47 530
D1950	47 259	47 552
D1956	47 260	47 553
D1957	47 261	47 554
D1628	47 046	47 601

Many of these locomotives did not carry their intermediate numbers.

The remaining left/middle column data from Table 19:

Original No.	Renumbering
D1571	47 453
D1572/3	47 018/9
D1574–82	47 454–62
D1583	47 020
D1584	47 531
D1585	47 542
D1586/7	47 463/4
D1588	47 543
D1589/90	47 465/6
D1591	47 024
D1592	47 544
D1593–6	47 467–70
D1597	47 026
D1598	47 471
D1599	47 027
D1600–4	47 472–6
D1605	47 028
D1606	47 029
D1607/8	47 477/8
D1609–11	47 030–2
D1612	47 479
D1613–5	47 033–5
D1616	47 480
D1617–26	47 036–45
D1627	47 481
D1628–35	47 046–53
D1636/7	47 482/3
D1638–40	47 054–6
D1641	47 532
D1642	47 547
D1643–5	47 059–61
D1646	47 545
D1647/8	47 063/4
D1649	47 535
D1650	47 066
D1651	47 533
D1652–4	47 068–70
D1655	47 536

Original No.	Renumbering
D1714	47 124
D1715	47 548
D1716	47 489
D1717	47 126
D1718	47 539
D1719	47 128
D1720–2	47 129–31
D1723	47 540
D1724	47 549
D1725	47 490
D1726–30	47 134–8
D1731	47 550
D1732/3	47 140/1
D1734	withdrawn
D1735–45	47 142–52
D1746	47 551
D1747	47 546
D1748–52	47 155–9
D1753	47 491
D1754	47 160
D1755	47 541
D1756–9	47 162–5
D1760	47 492
D1761–81	47 166–86
D1782–1836	47 301–55
D1837–74	47 187–224
D1875–1900	47 330–81
D1901–7	47 225–31
D1908	withdrawn
D1909–29	47 206–26
D1930	47 530
D1931	47 254
D1932	47 493
D1933–5	47 255–7
D1936/7	47 494/5
D1938	47 258
D1939–49	47 496–506

CHAPTER 7

TWO PROTOTYPES — *LION* AND *KESTREL*

The most elusive of the two Sulzer-engined private venture prototype locomotives was the white liveried Co-Co named *Lion*, which was unveiled publicly in the spring of 1962. Built at the Smethwick works of BRCW, it was BRCW locomotive No DEL260. Following the trend set in 1957 by the two EE prototype shunters which took their running numbers from their Vulcan Foundry numbers (D226/7) and Brush traction No 280 *Falcon* of 1961, which was numbered D0280, *Lion* became D0260.

Lion was the result of ER requirements for a new type 4 with Co-Co rather than 1Co-Co1 layout, and followed a period in which, among others, a Crewe-built diesel-electric version of the WR Western class diesel-hydraulic was proposed;

Below: Outline published in 1961 showing the then proposed second generation type 4 diesel-electric for BR. The close similarity to *Lion* is very apparent and suggests that this locomotive was originally intended to be the design to be adopted by BR rather than the Brush class 47. *(Collection of B. Webb)*

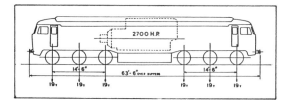

Below: The BRCW–Sulzer–AEI 2750bhp prototype Co-Co diesel-electric locomotive *Lion* climbing the Lickey incline with a test train, including a dynamometer car, during August 1962. *(GEC Traction)*

numbers D1200–58 were alloted to this unusual proposal. The undesirability of having twinned engine-generator sets and using the high-speed, high-maintenance cost Bristol-Siddeley Maybach engine, as in the Brush locomotive *Falcon*, was the main reason for this idea lapsing.

The very marked similarity of *Lion* to the appearance of the Beyer, Peacock (Hymek) Ltd class 35 1700bhp diesel hydro-mechanical locomotives of the WR was due to their both being styled by the same designer.

Lion was acclaimed as the most powerful single-engined diesel-electric locomotive ever built, using the latest version of the Sulzer twin-bank engine rated at 2750bhp. It was built within the new BR type 4 specification for a 114-ton Co-Co, and due to this had the same overall dimensions as the Brush type 4 or class 47 Co-Co which was to appear later that year from Loughborough weighing more than the stipulated weight. Both mechanically and technically *Lion* was a very different beast from the class 47, and apart from the likeness quoted above and a common engine make, it was designed quite separately by a consortium very divorced from Loughborough, in spite of much conjecture otherwise. The joint efforts of the design and technical expertise of BRCW, Sulzer Bros and AEI were brought together to good effect and it has been opined, at least privately, that a superior locomotive in every way to the class 47 was in fact produced, albeit about two years too late. Sulzer, though, shrewdly had their engines in both!

Lion introduced some new features into British

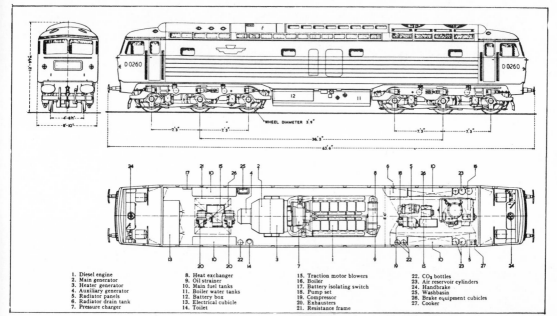

1. Diesel engine	8. Heat exchanger	15. Traction motor blowers	22. CO₂ bottles
2. Main generator	9. Oil strainer	16. Boiler	23. Air reservoir cylinders
3. Heater generator	10. Main fuel tanks	17. Battery isolating switch	24. Handbrake
4. Auxiliary generator	11. Boiler water tanks	18. Pump set	25. Washbasin
5. Radiator panels	12. Battery box	19. Compressor	26. Brake equipment cubicles
6. Radiator drain tank	13. Electrical cubicle	20. Exhausters	27. Cooker
7. Pressure charger	14. Toilet	21. Resistance frame	

Above: Side, end and plan views of *Lion*. It is interesting to compare this with class 47 and the upper diagram on the facing page.

(Collection of B. Webb)

diesel locomotive practice: a rubber bogie/super-structure suspension system; provision of dual train-heating, steam and electric; auxiliary/control equipment in removable/replaceable units; roof-mounted cooling system, also removable; lightweight body design of stressed steel; and glass-fibre roof traps and doors, etc. The mechanical structure made use of aircraft type load-bearing principles by using the full length bodysides between the headstocks as main load-bearing units. They were a welded assembly of mild steel plate and pressings, and as in the BR class 84 electric locomotives, this structure was described as a 'Virendeel Truss'. It was covered externally with a skin of 14-gauge steel plate. To avoid the rippled appearance common in rolling stock bodies, the skin was fluted below waist level.

The main bulkheads between the cabs and engine room were 3in thick, insulated with fibreglass wool. Insulated removable panels provided access to the control cubicle and train-heating boiler. The provision of only two cab rear-wall bulkheads and the omission of transverse bulkheads within the engine compartment improved

Right: A view of the superstructure of *Lion* in the BRCW works at Smethwick loaded with weights for strain-gauge tests in connection with 200-ton end-loadings.

(GEC Traction)

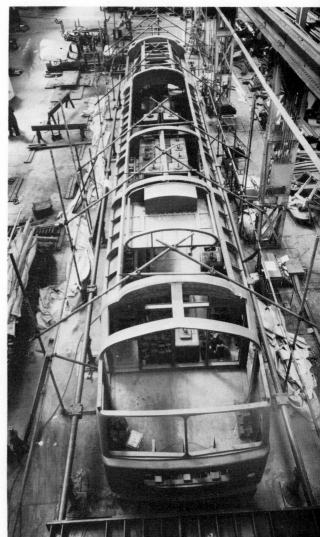

equipment location within the body. The underframe acted as engine bedplate and was an all-welded structure with Z-section solebars forming the bottom part of the bodyside girder running the full length of the locomotive. The bolster cross-bars and power unit cross-bars were between the solebars. Inner solebars of rolled-steel channel sections ran between the cross-members and carried the decking which also formed a drainage sump under the power unit. Pipework and cabling was accommodated in deck troughs. Over the decking plate was a false floor of chequered aluminium plates, for walkway use. This was arranged for easy removal for inspection purposes. After fabrication, the body was loaded with weights simulating the effect of power equipment and subjected to end loading of 200 tons—the figure desired by BR. Strain-gauge measurements proved the calculations, and stress levels were correct.

At No 1 end above the cant rail were two Serck engine-cooling water panels, air being drawn in through these by a pair of centrally located electrically-driven fans and ejected upwards through the roof. The whole unit was self-supporting and removable as a whole for maintenance. Under this was placed the Spanner Swirlyflow train-heating boiler unit, air reservoirs, radiator drain tank, Westinghouse air-compressor, a traction motor blower, the combined pump set and items of brake equipment. In the centre of the engine room was the engine/generator set. At No 2 end the main control cubicle was placed against the cab bulkhead. Between this and the engine/generator set were a second traction motor blower and two Northey exhauster sets. Above these was positioned further brake gear, and in the roof the load-regulator and some resistor units, the latter being cooled by air drawn in through louvres and emitted by roof ventilators. Fuel tanks were in pairs at each end of the engine room, but the water tanks for the train-heating boiler were underslung between the bogies. Behind hinged louvres above cant level were placed Intermit oil-wetted air-filters, through which entered all engine room air.

Above the engine room was a roof-trap fitted with translucent glass-fibre panels which could be unlocked under pneumatic control and raised 6in to allow hot air to escape from the engine room before any maintenance work was carried out. The Benton & Stone pneumatic unit incorporated an interlocking system which prevented the trap being raised when the locomotive was moving. The trap could be slid along in raised position to allow removal of pistons, etc. The cabs of *Lion* were similar externally to BR class 35 Hymek locomotives, being an all-steel structures with glass-fibre cab doors and roof mouldings.

The bogies incorporated the Alsthom system of twin rubber-cone body support pivots and radius-arm guided axleboxes. These items were used to give good riding qualities with a minimum of rubbing surfaces, thus reducing maintenance costs. A mild-steel fabricated bogie frame was used which was stress-relieved after welding. It was supported on four nests of helical coil springs on low-level equalising beams, which were carried from the axleboxes on combined shear and compression rubber pads. The latter assisted in reducing dead weight on the track to a minimum. The helical coil springs were controlled by shock absorbers. SKF roller-bearing axleboxes were fitted, each being supported by two Silentbloc bushed radius arms anchored to the bogie frames. This gave cushioning against fore-and-aft motion and lateral stability. On each bogie were two double-ended cone-rubber pivots resting in pockets in the bogie and main frame cross-members. Transverse stabilisers aligned the pivots vertically, these being secured between the pivots and the main frame. Part of the superstructure weight was carried on four spring-loaded side bearers, fitted with manganese-steel wearing pads, on the bogie frame. Adjustment of the weight was possible.

Braking consisted of vacuum-controlled locomotive air brakes operating in conjunction with the vacuum train brake. A straight air-brake independently operated was used for solo locomotive and unbraked trains. Westinghouse supplied all the brake equipment.

The electric traction equipment was by AEI, the generator consisting of three machines: traction, auxiliary and train-heating generators. These were arranged in tandem, the traction and train-heating generators and their armatures being on a common shaft supported by a single bearing in the traction generator end shield. The auxiliary generator was overhung from the traction generator, its armature being placed on an extension of the main shaft. It was this generator unit which contributed to the locomotive coming within the permitted 19-ton axle loading, for it employed silicone insulating materials which enabled the size and weight of the equipment to

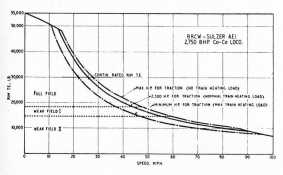

Exploded view of *Lion* showing lifting roof section
and also cab layout.   *(GEC Traction)*

be kept low. The traction generator was of AEI
type TG5303, continuously rated at 496V, 3500A,
at 1150rpm and 780V, 2245A, 1150rpm one-hour
rating. This supplied power, under control of the
automatic load-regulator, to the six traction
motors which were connected permanently in
parallel. The traction generator was of a new
AEI type incorporating some new features to
achieve savings in copper content and weight, the
armature being shorter but greater in diameter
and resulting in a more compact frame. The
machine had a separately-excited field winding

which had its field strength adjusted by the load
regulator. The generator was said to have a
special series field winding consisting of bars
fitted in the main pole face connected in series to
bars clamped on one side of the interpoles, and
formed into two parallel paths in series with the
armature. The current in this winding produced
the necessary decompounding field which in conjunction with the separately-excited field gave the
required output characteristic, also producing
the flux for the commutating field and compensation of armature reaction, and finally serving as a
starting winding when motoring the generator
from the battery at engine starting.

AEI claimed that the armature winding was
also special. It was of radial type with each con-
ductor placed so that it occupied the full width of
the armature slot. This reduced eddy current
losses and improved the space factor compared
with the usual 'side by side' winding. Cooling air
was passed between the risers connecting the ·
commutator with the armature coils. This
allowed the generator to produce a high continuous rating current.

Both traction and train-heating generators had
Pollock type commutators to give radial stability

of the copper segments which were clamped throughout their length; this made the segments shorter because the creepage distances were vertical to the machine axis. A further reduction in copper content added to weight saving already achieved.

The train-heating generator was of AEI type AG106 rated continuously at 800V, 480A, 690/1150rpm. Due to the intermittent nature of eth loading, steps were made to give it additional work to do to avoid possible commutator deterioration resulting from light running. To this end the eth generator also provided current for the radiator fan motors and traction motor blower motors; it also was used for main generator field excitation which, being included in the 800V power system, allowed reduced currents to be handled by the load-regulator. The fan and blower motors were arranged for either series or parallel operation, depending upon the output required from the power unit. This reduced auxiliary machine noise when the locomotive was working at low power within station confines. The auxiliary generator was of AEI type AG105 rated at 110V, 382A, at 500–1150rpm. This unit operated four machines: the combined pump set, two Northey type 125RE/FM two-speed rotary vacuum exhausters for the train vacuum braking system and the Westinghouse air-compressor supplying air at 100lb/sq in for locomotive air brake, locomotive control system, heating for the driving cabs and locomotive lighting.

Control equipment, developed from that in classes 24 and 25, was mainly housed in a pre-wired cubicle sub-assembly. The electrically driven load-regulator was, with its associated gear, mounted in a section built into the removable roof above the auxiliary machines at No 2 end.

The six AEI type 253 traction motors fitted to *Lion* were the first fitted to a BR locomotive. This motor was designed for many rail gauges and is often termed a 'narrow gauge' motor. Its small size is apparent in the accompanying illustrations of the locomotive bogie. They were nose-suspended, axle-hung machines with forced ventilation. In this application they had two stages of field weakening which, in conjunction with an axle:driving gear ratio of 17:70, gave a service speed of 100mph. Despite the compact size and low weight, the motor gave high torque and power output, rated continuously at 355hp at 495V, 585A, at 790rpm (full-field); and 360hp, 495V, at 1305rpm (weak field with 58 per cent

divert). Class 'H' silicone insulation was used and the ventilating air was routed to give maximum cooling efficiency, these also contributing to weight saving.

Lion was first seen publicly in April 1962. Its construction took a long time, so that even before its appearance the chances of it being ordered for BR were slight. It was sent to Marylebone on 28 May 1962 for inspection by BR officials and Crown Agents officials because it was hoped that it had an export potential. Prior to inspection *Lion* had been running-in on the Birmingham–Shrewsbury and Banbury routes with loads of 16, 18 and 20 coaches, at high and low speeds. Tests on the Lickey incline demonstrated its ability to stop and restart such loads on the 1 in 37 gradient. Speeds of up to 17mph at the summit with 20 coaches (639 tons) and 20mph with 16 coaches (519 tons) were attained easily. At three-quarter power *Lion* reached 81mph with a 582½-ton load and 90mph with 639 tons.

In May *Lion* was allocated to the WR at Wolverhampton Stafford Road depot and was made ready for running on the Birmingham–Wolverhampton–Paddington services. On 14 May it took on the 07.25 at Wolverhampton and by arrival in London had gained 16 minutes of a loss of 17 minutes caused by signal checks.

A fault in the electrical system on 17 May caused the cancellation at Leamington of the 90min Birmingham–Paddington run, and it returned to BRCW for attention. *Lion* was able to take 400 tons at over 100mph with ease. In June further tests on the Lickey were made, followed by transfer to Swindon for road testing with the dynamometer car. These resulted in *Lion* working to Paddington and Cheltenham, followed by tests in South Devon. On 14 August it ran to Plymouth with 16 coaches and took part in runs with similar loads with stop/start tests on Rattery and Hemerdon banks.

Lion vanished into the BRCW works in September 1962, not to reappear until April 1963 with test trains on the Birmingham–Leamington route, and in August did further trails over the Lickey incline, passing to the ER at Finsbury Park in September. During its short spell on the ER, *Lion* worked from King's Cross on various local trains to Peterborough, and also the 'Master Cutler' to Sheffield and 'Yorkshire Pullman' to Leeds.

Lion did little running on BR, due partly to BRCW financial problems and design deficiencies. At one point inadequate design in the diesel

On one of its very few
service train runs, D0260
Lion, with its white and
gold livery decidedly
grimy, pulls away from
Leeds Central with the up
'Yorkshire Pullman' in
September 1963.
(GEC Traction)

engine resulted in oil contamination of the main
generators and flashovers. This damaged the
generator insulation and caused the commutator
bars to tilt and resulted in an abrasive action on
the brush gear. The main generator was prone to
periodic overheating due mainly to the 800V
excitation system provided from the eth generator, this resulting in insulation problems in the
load regulator. A lesson was learned from this
exercise and the idea has not been repeated. The
main generator used was the first attempt by AEI
at a high power machine, it being opined that
powers such as 2750bhp are now better dealt
with by alternators. With the problems increasing in *Lion's* equipment and little point in carrying out extensive modifications in view of little
chance of orders, the locomotive was sent to
Doncaster works in October 1963, before returning to BRCW. By this time BR was committed to
its 'second generation type 4' with heavy ordering
of class 47s from Brush and BR Crewe.

Lion was subsequently dismantled at the
BRCW works to help pay off creditors. Reusable
components were salvaged, Sulzer Bros took
back the diesel engine, and train-heating boiler
too for some strange reason, the engine being
sent to Vickers Ltd at Barrow for overhaul before
being supplied to BR as a spare for class 47
D1500–19; like *Lion* they were eth equipped and
as a result had engines with longer sideframes
than the post-D1520 production locomotives.

AEI took back the generator group and traction motors and, although the memory of *Lion*
lingers, AEI took steps in 1966 to extinguish this
by ordering the locomotive's nameplates to be
melted down to prevent them falling into the

hands of collectors, at least one of these attrac-
tive mementos receiving this fate.

AEI considered *Lion* one of its less successful
ventures and a cloud shrouds its history. Why
this should be so, in view of the long and successful history of AEI and its constituents in modern
rail traction, is left to conjecture. *Lion* was a
purely private venture on behalf of the three
manufacturers concerned, but it was designed for
the BR market and conformed to the BR Design
Panel requirements. It was a make or break
venture for its ailing mechanical parts maker,
desperate for orders to occupy its large works.
The design remained at all times under the control of the consortium, and no trading of ideas or
of design staff took place between this and BR or
with Brush. The design staff of BRCW mainly
joined the Sulzer group with an office at the
Saltley works of Metropolitan-Cammell, and
later had a separate office in Birmingham until
1976. Such designs as the Sulzer–AEI–Metro-
Cammell Zambesi class for Africa, and some
projected designs incorporating the then mooted
R series engines in the 1700–2300bhp range,
emanated from this period.

The second Sulzer-powered prototype was
more of an embarrassment than a too-late design
for BR. Great interest was aroused during 1966
when it became known that Brush Traction Ltd
was building a 4000bhp locomotive at its Loughborough plant. This locomotive was completed
in late 1967, and, built in the hope that a world
market existed for high-power diesel-electrics,
Brush, with Sulzer, had the courage to go ahead
and build it. In common with previous Brush
prototypes this locomotive was given the name of

a bird of prey, in this case *Kestrel*.

Although *Kestrel* was a private venture, BR was considerably involved in its evolution. It drew on the LVA24 engine, a new range of Brush electrical equipment, and electronic systems developed from work undertaken on the experimental Bo-Bo diesel-electric *Hawk*, which itself was the rebuild of the 1950-built North British/ Paxman/BTH 827hp locomotive No 10800 with a Bristol-Siddeley Maybach 1400bhp engine and Brush electrical equipment.

Kestrel was the first ac/dc diesel-electric locomotive to run on BR. Numbered HS4000, to remind everyone that its builder was a member of the Hawker-Siddeley Group, it was painted in chocolate-brown and yellow livery, its name being painted in large letters centrally on each side. Designed for rail gauges up to 5ft 6in, *Kestrel* was based mechanically on the BR class 47 design involving the chassisless monocoque stressed-skin body which was fully load-bearing and designed for a 200-ton centre buffing load.

New features were involved in locomotive cab design, layout of controls, legibility of instruments and sound insulation for crew comfort, involving sound-deadening bulkheads between cabs and engine room, semi-resiliently rubber-mounted cab fixings and three layers of sound insulating material. Cab heating was by 4kW

heaters, plus additional foot warmers, and thermostatically controlled at a cut-off point of 72°F, while internal pressurisation was sufficient to keep out draughts and dust. Externally the cab was the locomotive's most distinguishing feature: gone was the slab-front of the class 47 and class 50; instead a semi-streamlined unit with wrap-round windscreen was provided, Triplex supplying the laminated glass as a special job.

Kestrel was only 3ft 0in longer than the class 47, but represented an almost doubled power output in conventional diesel-electric equipment, and around 50 per cent increase in power over single-engine diesel-electric equipment; and it was within accepted European axle loadings. Principal improvements in mechanical design were the underslinging of oil-fuel tanks, use of dry inertia-type air filters instead of oil-wetted panels to obtain a dry oil-free compartment.

Technically the locomotive was notable for several innovative design features, employing the highest-powered ac/dc transmission for rail traction in the world. The control equipment was based on a large proportion of static electronic units of plug-in type which were easily checked and replaced. Continuously variable power-control and automatic proportioning of friction and electric-dynamic braking was available through a single control lever. Some auxiliaries were driven by three-phase squirrel cage ac motors. The interior of the locomotive was also lightly pressurised to prevent dust ingress, and heated and ventilated.

Bogies of Commonwealth cast-steel type were

The Hawker-Siddeley/Brush Traction prototype locomotive *Kestrel,* with its original bogies but regauged to USSR 5ft gauge and on exhibition in July. 1971 at the USSR Railway Exhibition at Scherbinka
(Brush Electrical Machines)

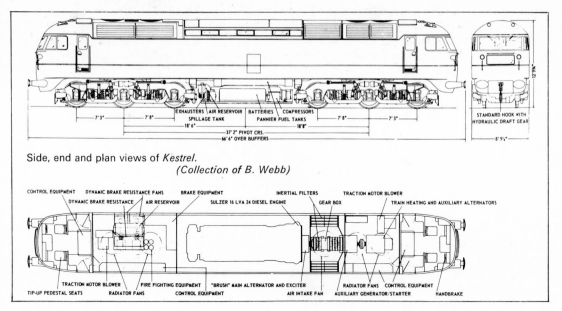

Side, end and plan views of *Kestrel*.
(Collection of B. Webb)

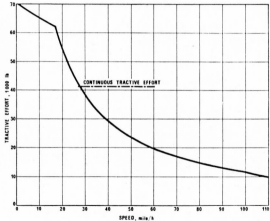

5ft 0in longer in wheelbase than those of class 47. They had overslung equalising beams as used in the prototype locomotive *Falcon*, the class 47 having underslung beams. The axleboxes had SKF bearings, the outer axles with double-row, single-width, self-aligning bearings and the centre axle with double-row, cylindrical roller-bearings. The springing of the bogie frame was by coil springs. Tyre profiles were of BR-Heumann type. The body weight was supported on a cast-steel bolster with a large centre-bearing fitted with a Railko disc. Side bearers only catered for emergency conditions.

Kestrel was powered by the 16LVA24 Sulzer engine, one of three built at Winterthur, which passed its UIC 100-hour test in March 1967, and

which was in fact a development of the 8- and 12-cylinder LVA24 engines running in the SNCF locomotives of classes 66501 and 68000, of Bo-Bo and A1A-A1A layout respectively. In *Kestrel* its metric rating was 4000hp, but in the UK 3946bhp. The engine was resiliently mounted on Metalastic units.

Engine cooling comprised two twin-bank radiator panels at No 1 end and two single-bank panels at No 2 end, air being drawn through No 1 end by two 40in diameter roof-mounted cooling fans between the panels, electrically driven by squirrel-cage motors, hot air leaving vertically at high velocity to obviate recirculation. Fan motor control was electronic with solid-state temperature detection, which brought in one or two fans as water temperature rose, and also opened or closed the relevant compressed-air operated radiator shutters. At No 2 end two 36in diameter fans controlled from the secondary cooling circuit were fitted. The cooling system was by Serck-Visco with electronic control by Brush and fans by Keith Blackman Ltd.

Electric traction equipment was by Brush. The main alternator was directly coupled to the engine crankshaft, the stator was flange-mounted to the engine casing and supported on feet bolted through flexible mountings to the locomotive floor plate. A flexible coupling drove, via a 2·5:1 step-up gear, the high-speed output shaft of which drove the auxiliary alternator and dynastarter. The latter motored the diesel engine at starting and provided dc power for charging the batteries, engine priming pumps, exhausters and compressors. The dynastarter had a continuous output at maximum engine speed of 448A, 110V, 4·93kW. A right-angle drive from a gearbox drove a pressurising fan at 1·66 times engine speed.

The combined auxiliary and train-heating alternator with brushless exciter had three three-phase starter windings which supplied power via rectifiers for train-heating, one winding also supplying power for auxiliaries. The output was 533kVA, 680V ac at maximum rpm; each of the three windings was switched in sequence through Westinghouse rectifiers to provide a constant 825V dc for train heating. The main alternator was a ten-pole three-phase salient-pole unit with a rotating armature brushless ac exciter. The ac output being rectified by 84 300A silicon diodes mounted on the end of the main rotor shaft and three-phase bridge-connected. Ac/dc power supply had a continuous rating output at maximum engine rpm of 1100, of 3110A, 810V, 2520kW, or 4980A, 504V, 2510kW, according to loading. Protection included a short-circuit switch on the main alternator winding with an electronic control to divert flashover current away from the traction motor, an innovation resulting from the work on the experimental locomotive *Hawk*.

The six Brush parallel-connected traction motors of four-pole type were dc series-wound machines with forced ventilation supplied by a 20hp squirrel-cage motored blower of three-phase type. They were axle-mounted by the suspension-tube system concentric with their respective axles, and were flexibly mounted on Silent-bloc rubber bushes. The suspension was by nose links top and bottom, the centre motor being arranged to permit lateral movement of wheel and motor set. Drive was via resilient gears enclosed in an oil-bath with a ratio of 19:60. The design of the motors followed usual Brush practice, and they were rated at 515hp, 504V, 830A, at 681rpm, or 510hp, 464V, 900A, at 610rpm.

Kestrel had a wheelslip detector unit which compared current balance in the traction motors by measuring with dc transducers, but further development work was in hand which provided a speedier corrective action. Wheelslip correction was obtained by reducing automatically the alternator excitation, this being restored again at a controlled rate once the wheel slipping had been checked.

Braking was arranged to include a powerful rheostatic system of 1470kW in two equal resistor banks. The brake system control proportioned continuously the locomotive friction and dynamic brake forces automatically through a single brake handle.

Kestrel was handed-over for service trials on BR at Marylebone Station by Sir Arnold Hall, Chairman and Managing Director of Hawker-Siddeley, and F. H. Wood, Chairman and Managing Director of Brush Electrical Engineering Co. Ltd, on 29 January 1968; Sir Henry Johnson, Chairman of the board, received the locomotive on behalf of British Rail.

The locomotive had been weighed at Derby works on 20 January, when its major disadvantage to BR was discovered, being at 133 tons service weight in excess of the BR axle-loading limits of 20 tons. So, although designed for high-speed performance of up to 130mph, it was never exactly tested in this area. BR thinking was that, with locomotives having nose-suspended traction motors designed for 100mph-plus running, an axle-loading of less than 20 tons was desirable. One reason for *Kestrel*'s excess weight was the large proportion of prototype equipment incorporated—always difficult to control as regards weight in pre-production items.

Initial testing was undertaken at Derby and on the LMR West Coast main line in early 1968, when loads of empty coaches were taken over Shap. On 8 May a 660-ton load of 24 coaches was taken up Shap at 46mph. On 15 May, *Kestrel* was handed over to the ER and allocated to Tinsley, but in fact was based at Shirebrook for heavy freight duties. It performed this task well, but was hardly taxed to capacity because the majority of its trains were similar to those taken by other BR diesels, it being operationally impossible to marshall trains adequately heavy for *Kestrel*. The Shirebrook–Whitemoor (March) route was to be the locomotive's principal haunt on BR, with loads of 1450–1600 tons and two round trips daily for five days a week, loaded on the up run and empty on the return. Speeds of 35 to 40mph made full power use very rare indeed, but the locomotive was doing some six-million train ton miles per month. Completing 364 miles per day, *Kestrel* had covered some 14,000 miles by mid-August 1968, hauled 118,508 tons of coal and attained an availability of 88 per cent.

During August a much-publicised special load was arranged for *Kestrel*, comprising 52 BR 32-ton hopper wagons over the Mansfield–Lincoln

route, and weighing 2028 tons. *Kestrel* successfully restarted this on the 1 in 150 Broughton bank in wet conditions and accelerated to 15mph in seven minutes, wheelslip being controlled by the automatic anti-slip device when slipping occurred at three-quarter open controller setting. On the return run the load was restarted on Marham bank in dry conditions, during which the locomotive developed full power for eight minutes. Although claimed to be the heaviest load ever hauled on BR by one locomotive, it only just exceeded that of a GWR 2800 class 2-8-0, which on test hauled a 2012-ton load on 25 February 1906, admittedly on a level route.

In August and September 1968, *Kestrel* was involved in both static and running tests on BR, covering hundreds of miles at constant power and speed, the load consisting of a train of electrically-braked mobile testing units supplemented by the rheostatic brake power of class 86 electric locomotive E3122. The electric locomotive also hauled the train with *Kestrel* at the rear to test its dynamic brake. No special high-speed running was done, the tests concentrating on locomotive performance related to normal BR requirements and being carried out on the Derby–Stoke–Crewe–Nuneaton–Derby route, but 102mph was recorded. Upon completion of the test programme it returned to its plodding coal train duties from Shirebrook depot, so that by the end of 1968 it had done 26,000 miles, of which 22,000 were revenue-earning, and accumulated 1731 engine hours.

In order to make *Kestrel* acceptable for passenger service something had to be done to reduce its weight to permit regular running at over 70mph. It was decided to fit class 47 bogies to bring axle-loading down, this being carried out at Loughborough in May/June 1969. This did the trick, but in addition modified the locomotive's continuous rating due to the bogies having the smaller class 47 motors. Following conversion, during July, a series of test runs on the East Coast main line, with Shirebrook drivers and inspectors to familiarise the crews, were undertaken. On one run *Kestrel* climbed Stoke bank (1 in 178 gradient) at over 100mph, hauling a train of Pullman stock.

Driver training at Finsbury Park permitted the locomotive to spend a short period on the East Coast main line, commencing on 20 October 1969 with the 07.55 King's Cross–Newcastle and 16.45 return. In mid-1970 *Kestrel* was performing on London–Hull Freightliner trains. In June 1971 the locomotive was sent to Vickers factory at Barrow for engine removal and overhaul under Sulzer supervision, returning to its Mansfield–Whitemoor duties for most of the final phase of its BR career.

Static and running tests reports indicated that *Kestrel* was a good locomotive, but that the Sulzer engine was 170bhp less than the specified

4000 metric hp or 3945bhp. This 4·3 per cent reduction gave 3775bhp, arrived at by adding the 3412hp at main alternator input, 215hp auxiliary alternator input, 58hp dynastarter input and pressurising fan input of 90hp. Fuel consumption was 1,391lb/hour, and engine maximum efficiency was around 800rpm at about half-power. The cooling system was found adequate for sustained full-power operation in temperatures up to 86°F, and it was opined that the pressurised system was not really necessary under UK conditions.

Traction motor ratings were found to be actually 870A continuous, 885A at one-hour rating and 1125A at 20-minute rating. The main alternator ran cool at all times and, together with the traction motors, the ac/dc auxiliaries, compressors, exhausters, etc., all produced reliable test performances, demonstrating fully the advantages of ac/dc power.

Troubles with fuses blowing during sustained traction motor heating tests at Derby and Loughborough occurred at 7200A and during short duration adhesion tests at 8250A. Some rectifier troubles were due to failure of protective devices; improvements to air supply were made to overcome this. The electronic control system proved sensitive and stable for engine control and alternator output over the complete power/speed range, although some lack of reliability in connections and components was experienced.

Adhesion at low speeds was good, and tractive efforts up to 85,900lb were measured on dry rails for ten seconds at 10·3mph. The locomotive resistance was low at 11lb/ton at 80mph. Automatic weight-transfer compensation was not found to be a significant advantage in *Kestrel*, but the automatic wheelslip device was responsible in arresting slipping due to poor track conditions; in wet conditions the highest tractive effort was sustained by using the driver's anti-slip air brake. There were two methods of slip control:

the driver's anti-slip button applying anti-slip brake and weight transfers compensation, and the electronic wheelslip detector applying anti-slip brake and automatic power reduction.

Riding qualities in the vertical plane were possible of improvement at over 75mph, while secondary damping was probably excessive. At 100mph in the lateral plane riding was acceptable. The bogies were lively but rotationally stable, *Kestrel* undergoing bogie-rotational tests on the Darlington Bank Top calibrated turntable in May 1968.

In 1971 *Kestrel* was sold to the USSR railways and following attention at Crewe works and alteration of its original bogies to 5ft 0in gauge it was packed ready for shipment. It was towed from Crewe depot to Cardiff docks on a pair of spare class 47 bogies and shipped from there to Leningrad on 8 July 1971. *Kestrel* was exhibited at the 1971 USSR Railway Exhibition at Scherbinka during July, being officially handed over to the USSR by F. H. Wood, then Chairman of the Railway Industry Association of Great Britain, and of Brush Electrical Engineering Co. Ltd. As expected, little has been heard of *Kestrel* since, but it is suggested that after testing it was dismantled for examination and its techniques evaluated prior to being incorporated into Soviet diesel traction work. In conjunction with the export of British locomotives to Cuba and the building of BR locomotives in Romania, it would appear that a hybrid 4000bhp diesel-electric is now in production for use in Eastern-Bloc countries.

The agreement of 1969 between Sulzer and EE for the further development of the LVA24 engine range was not to produce any results apart from giving EE the Sulzer experience with this engine and, one could say, effectively preventing any further high-power Sulzer engined locomotives from a competitive manufacturer.

Goodbye *Kestrel*. After failing to impress BR by having no real advantages over the Deltic locomotives, it was sold to the USSR. Here suitably packed it awaits towing to Cardiff Docks at Crewe depot in July 1971.   *(Allan C. Baker)*

CHAPTER 8
THE SULZERS AT WORK

The subject of locomotive performance often provokes argument and opinions as to which formulae should be used to calculate the results, and it is not the intention here to enter into the argument. The Sulzer locomotives on BR, like their counterparts from other manufacturers, have their off times, but the contents of this chapter has been chosen from the observations of Michael J. Oakley, a specialist in this field, to indicate just what they can do.

When secondary locomotives of classes 24 and 25 spend most of their time on freight trains they are difficult to assess, except in Scotland on the Highland lines and in Wales on the Cambrian lines. In Scotland at Inverness class 24 was often paired with class 26 on heavy workings northwards, but used singly on the Wick and Kyle lines. In April 1972, two class 24s, D5129 and D5121, with 242/250 tons tare/gross, increasing to 255 tons, on the 08.20 Inverness–Edinburgh, demonstrated their medium- to high-speed capability with a relatively light load. Climbing the repeated initial 1 in 60 sections to Slochd summit, an estimated drawbar horsepower (edbhp) of a modest 1618 at 41mph improved as the locomotives warmed up. From a stop at Tomatin, due to a late-running down train, D5129 and D5121 put in the best climb of the run by increasing to 40mph and giving an edbhp of 1745 at 32mph at Slochd, the remainder of the run to Perth being executed similarly, but with little sustained high-speed running. A stop at Perth, due to loose brake rigging, resulted in some sustained attempts to regain time. The climb to Gleneagles, mainly 1 in 100, was stormed at a minimum 52mph; on a similar grade at Polmont, 48mph was attained. On the final virtually level section to Edinburgh 84mph was reached near Saughton Junction, but power output had fallen at this speed to 1391 edbhp at 54mph, and only 923 at 77mph.

On the Cambrian lines the class 24s mainly worked light trains, but on summer Saturdays the London trains ran with up to ten coaches and one locomotive until demand increased loadings and brought in multiple working. In August 1972, D5082, with a ten-coach load, 349/365 tons increasing to 380, put in a consistently good performance. It took the 10.05 Aberystwyth–

Euston up the severe 1 in 51 to Talerddig sustaining 16½mph, while 60mph was reached on the undulating track past Montgomery. The 30/32mph minimum on the 1 in 80/100 past Breidden was very good, while edbhp fell no more than from 858 at 16mph to 740 at 55mph. A maximum of 71mph was reached at Yockleton on the last few miles into Shrewsbury. The class 25, with higher engine power and 90mph as opposed to 75mph top speed, is less powerful at low speeds, and rarely is less than a pair found on passenger work, that is when found at all.

An exceptional run with D7571 on a type 4 roster with the 10.35 Portsmouth–Sheffield between Nottingham and Sheffield, loaded to nine coaches, 307/325 tons, was timed in July 1971:

Log 1
Train: 10.35 Portsmouth–Sheffield
Locomotive: D7571 ; nine coaches

M. Ch.	Location	Min. Sec.	Speed M	Edbhp/ mph
0 00	Nottingham	0 00		
0 56	Mansfield Jcn	3 05	30/36 (sigs)	
2 07	Radford	5 40	33	
3 51	Wollaton	8 21	34	928/34
5 14	Milepost 128¾	10 53	45/53 (sigs)	
7 16	Trowell	14 15	18	
8 53	Ilkeston Jcn	16 36	44	
10 36	Shipley Gate	18 53	50	
11 74	Langley Mill	20 30	53	
14 46	Codnor Park	23 27	56	
15 40	Pye Bridge	24 26	54/51	
18 08	Alfreton	27 25	52	
19 10	Westhouses	28 38	59	
21 07	Morton	30 43	55/64	744/56½
24 20	Clay Cross	34 23	28	
26 16	Hasland	36 51	59/64	
28 20	Chesterfield=39¼	39 57		
1 59	Sheepbridge	3 07	50	919/45
3 74	Unstone	6 01	37	
5 25	Dronfield	8 13	36/38	
6 30	Bradway Tunnel South	10 01	36/56	
8 01	Dore and Totley	12 09	43	
9 42	Millhouses	13 47	66/72	
10 72	Heeley	14 58	62	
12 22	Sheffield	18 49	—	

The edbhp outputs of 928 at 34mph on the 1 in 103 to Wollaton, and 919 at 45mph on 1 in 100 to Bradway tunnel were good slow-speed work for D7571. Climbing the varying Erewash Valley, Trowell to Morton saw a rapid fall in effort with edbhp at 744 at 56½mph. A four-and-a-half minute late arrival at Chesterfield was reduced by two minutes by the time Sheffield was reached.

An even more daunting task—rarely with a class 25 on the West Coast main line over Shap, also a type 4 job—saw D7585, in April 1972, take the much lighter five coaches of Mk II stock weighing 175/185 tons and forming the 14.20 Euston–Carlisle from Preston. D7585 attained 86mph on the almost level section to Lancaster, putting out 871 edbhp at 85mph. Passing Tebay at 79mph, the low-geared class 25 was found wanting on the 1 in 75 of Shap, but at Scout Green edbhp had only dropped to 858 at 56½mph, and the summit was taken at 43mph. The 32 miles 13 chains Oxenholme–Penrith section was covered in 32min 23sec, and at Wreay, just before Carlisle, 92mph was reached.

The class 26 and 27 from BRCW, although built to the same specification as classes 24 and 25, differ considerably in performance. The class 26 is effectively lower-geared than the class 24, and so is useful in the Highlands. In April 1973, D5308 of Haymarket, unusually working north of Inverness on a Sunday newspaper train, seven coaches 219/222 tons, was an extreme example. D5308 took the nasty climb from Invershin to the request stop at Lairgg, with its 1 in 72 grade, with an edbhp of 744 at 29mph, but on the undulating track elsewhere it was unable to reach 60mph more than once; earlier at Edderton, output dropped to 250 edbhp at 55mph.

For this reason it was usual Inverness practice to use class 26 paired with a class 24, combining the best of both types in the speed curve; however, two 26s in multiple was another matter. A case in point in April 1974 was locomotives 26046 and D5344 on the down 'Royal Highlander', with its unreasonably heavy 16 coaches giving 577/610 tons on the Perth–Inverness section. Leaving Perth seven-and-a-half minutes late, and in spite of the damp morning causing occasional slipping on the banks, seven minutes were regained by Inverness. Speeds rarely reached to 60mph but uphill work was stupendous. The long climb from Blair Atholl to milepost 49 finished with five miles of 1 in 70 on which speed settled to 29mph, slipped to 27½mph, then re-attained 28mph while still on the gradient. The final climb, Carr Bridge–Slochd, although shorter, has two miles of 1 in 60 on which 25½mph was attained before slipping again intervened. Taking these speeds as sustained gives edbhp outputs of 2000 and 2086, the latter being in excess of the rated maximum performance by at least a quarter. This is typical of the CP-equipped Sulzers with their magnificently vocal performances over the Highland lines, in which they always put out that little bit extra, and consistently develop horsepowers in excess of their theoretical limit.

The GEC-equipped BRCW locomotives of class 27 are of 1250bhp against 1160bhp of the class 26; and, although their output is more distributed through their speed curve to suit their 90mph maximum, they are no better than the class 26 at low speeds, but will maintain their power output well into the upper speed range.

An April 1977 runs with 27011 on the Sunday 18.10 Glasgow–Aberdeen with nine Mk II coaches, 296/315 tons, was a case of standing-in for a type 4. With a last-minute substitution and no banker available at Glasgow Queen Street, with its short platforms, 25234 was put on to pilot the train as far as Cowlairs Box, while a false alarm by the locomotive's fire bell at Lenzie was another problem. Speed rose steadily on the slight rise as far as Greenhill, giving edbhp of 978 at 58mph and 943 at 69½mph. Following a permanent way slowing at the foot of Dunblane bank, with its steady several miles of 1 in 88, speed dropped, but was sustained at 34/32½mph with an edbhp of 944 at 33mph, illustrating how the power at the drawbar hardly alters across a good part of the locomotive's speed range.

Probably the best-known class 27 job is the high-speed push-and-pull service on the Edinburgh–Glasgow route. This operates with six-coach sets of Mk II stock and one locomotive at each end. They operate on schedules demanding 90mph sustained running and, as discussed earlier, have been found wanting on this work which their BRCW designers certainly did not envisage for them. An outstanding performance of July 1971 involving D5386 and D5403 follows:

Log 2

Train: 21.30 Edinburgh–Glasgow
Locomotives: D5386 and D5403
Six coaches, 192/200 tons, Mk II stock

M. Ch.	Location	Min. Sec.	Speed	Edbhp/ mph
0 00	Edinburgh	0 00	—	
1 14	Haymarket	2 48	37 max	
2 09	Saughton Jcn	3 00	68	2026/76
4 20	Gogar	4 31	83	1626/81½
6 78	Ratho	6 34	91/94	
11 26	Winchburgh Jcn	9 27	85	
13 25	Philipstoun	10 49	89/95	
16 32	Linlithgow	12 48	92/89	
21 06	Polmont	15 53	92	
24 21	Falkirk High	18 37	—	

2 30	Rough Castle Box	3	04	73	2069/46½
4 38	Greenhill Upper Jcn	4	41	84	
6 25	Castlecary	5	54	91	1325/92
8 74	Dullatur	7	35	95	
10 27	Croy	8	30	92/96	
13 43	Waterside Jcn	10	32	94/92	
15 43	Lenzie	11	50	94	
18 46	Bishopbriggs	15	46	16	
				(sigs)	
19 71	Cowlairs Box	18	12	45	
21 59	Glasgow Queen				
	Street = 19	21	56	—	

On this run, calculated edbhp outputs of 2069 at 46½mph and 2026 at 76mph show remarkable flatness of the speed curve through the full output range. After passing the electrical unloading point the output fell rapidly, but only to 1626 edbhp at 81½mph and 1325edbhp at 92mph, giving ample power for the requirements of the schedule. These figures again do not correspond to rated performances.

The 1550bhp variant of the BRCW type 2 is the SR class 33. Being something of a general 'dogsbody' is has to shoulder a very wide range of duties, from four-coach Bournemouth–Weymouth express portions to ponderous slow excursions, all types of freight duty and, the most onerous duty, the Waterloo–Exeter service, where it replaced the WR Warship class diesel hydro-mechanical locomotives of 2200bhp. They still hold the fort on this work, but relief must be on the way as the HST attains (hopefully) its hopes and displaces type 4 locomotives.

D6509 with the 12.20 Exeter–Waterloo in October 1973, loaded to eight carriages, 282/290 tons, is typical of runs on this straight but violently undulating route, providing good opportunity for horsepower assessment. The first climb to Honiton, finishing with four miles of 1 in 100, saw D6509 give an edbhp of 1048 at 66½mph, while the long and varying climb to Axminster was done at an average of 60mph with a maximum of 88mph near Seaton Junction. The climb of 1 in 80 after the Sherborne stop saw a maximum of 36½mph, with a slightly lower output of 1029 edbhp at 35½mph, although a slight easing was probably to lessen slipping on the autumn leaves in the tree-lined cutting. From Andover the climb produced 1231edbhp at 50mph on a gradient of 1 in 781, although the line at this point ran on an exposed embankment so a following wind could have provided the excess. In comparing these figures with the performances of other classes, it is necessary to make allowance for train heating. In this case the train totalled 30 eth units, corresponding to about

195hp, and the latter figure should be added to the calculated edbhp before comparison with the bhp rating.

The large BR-built 1Co-Co1 Sulzers first appeared as the class 44, which was remarkably short-lived so far as passenger work is concerned, although they are used in emergencies. Their imminent demise in 1978 has found a clamouring for special workings and last runs. The best of these locomotives is the class 45, which, like the class 44, is CP equipped, while the Brush equipped derivative (class 46) is only a second best. The class 45s started their careers under the cloud of poor reliability, but today they are as good as, if not better, than later would-be usurpers, demonstrating very ably performances considerably in excess of their ratings, especially when running flat out with the heaviest trains available. Many runs to back these claims exist.

In June 1976, 45047 with the 21.14 (Sunday) Bristol–Glasgow/Edinburgh was loaded to 15 coaches, 548/575 tons. This sleeping-car train, normally restricted to 80mph but allowed only 115 minutes from Bristol to Birmingham (121 miles 18 chains), left Bristol 57 minutes late due to late connections. Not much was achieved by Bristol Parkway, but from thence onwards amends were made. Down the hill past Charfield 91/95mph was recorded with 1968edbhp at 82mph; up to 90mph was reached at Coaley and virtually maintained on the gradual rise between Eckington and Bromsgrove. Banked up the 1 in 37·7 of the Lickey incline by a pair of class 37s, the train sustained 30mph up the entire length of the bank—sustaining a total for all three locomotives of 4582edbhp. This run is typical of the work on this line, and 45047 wheeled the train into Birmingham New Street 46 minutes down on schedule.

The work of the class 45/1 locomotives with eth-equipped trains, heated by tapping the traction supply of the locomotive, is almost entirely on the LMR Midland line out of St Pancras. Running is mostly on nine-coach loads to Sheffield, requiring no exceptional outputs, but maximum-speed running is needed. A typical run of October 1973 found the 11.05 St Pancras–Sheffield headed by 45101 with a 300/315-ton load. With no real need to hurry, the 82 miles 74 chains to Market Harborough were covered in 71min 7sec, with a maximum of 100mph down the 1 in 200 descent to Bedford. On the dead-level past Loughborough 101mph was attained with ease. Uphill work was average, with edbhp outputs of 1766 at 73mph up the 1 in 176 to Elstree and 1643 at 81½mph on the 1 in 119 at Sharnbrook. The range of the speed curve is shown once again in the running north of Leicester, where the output fell only from 1824 edbhp at 60mph to 1485 at 95½mph. Once again it is necessary to add about 200hp for train heating from traction supply.

Log 3
Train: 11.05 St Pancras–Sheffield
Locomotive: 45 101
Nine coaches, 300/315 tons, eth 31, Mk II stock

M. Ch.	Location	Min.	Sec.	Speed	Edbhp/ mph
0 00	St Pancras	0	00	—	
1 42	Kentish Town	4	14	48/58	
5 09	Cricklewood	9	11	18 pws	
6 79	Hendon	11	09	67	
9 28	Mill Hill	13	12	71	
12 35	Elstree	15	46	73	1766/73
15 17	Radlett	17	46	94	
18 13	Napsbury	19	41	85	
19 71	St Albans	21	00	79	
21 20	Sandridge	22	03	78/89	
24 51	Harpenden	24	29	88/87	
27 22	Chiltern Green	26	13	96/84	
30 20	Luton	28	19	85/84	
32 62	Leagrave	30	07	86	
35 52	Sundon Box	32	02	97/100	
37 21	Harlington	33	01	99/96	
40 18	Flitwick	34	49	97	
41 60	Ampthill	35	47	98/99	
43 62	Millbrook Box	36	59	98	
47 18	Elstow GF	39	08	94/89	
49 77	Bedford North Jcn	40	56	93/94	
52 76	Oakley	42	54	89/97	
56 53	Sharnbrook	45	18	90	
58 11	Souldrop	46	21	82	1643/81½
59 60	Sharnbrook Summit	47	34	77	
62 53	Irchester	49	32	94	
65 05	Wellingborough	51	22	64	
69 28	Burton Latimer	54	46	85	
72 02	Kettering	59	26	10 pws	
74 46	Glendon South Jcn	62	47	56/66	
78 39	Desborough North Box	66	30	63/78 (sigs)	
82 74	Market Harborough	71	07	10 (sigs)	
86 25	East Langton	75	24	73/74	
89 55	Kibworth North	78	15	70	
91 43	Great Glen	79	36	86	
95 70	Wigston North Jcn	83	45	32/61 (sigs)	
99 05	Leicester=77¾	88	38	—	
0 59	Humberstone Road	1	39	46	1824/60
4 58	Syston	5	09	85 (sigs)	
7 42	Sileby	7	07	89	
9 66	Barrow-on-Soar	8	36	95	1485/95½
12 41	Loughborough	10	15	100/101	
15 26	Hathern	11	56	99/98	
17 24	Kegworth	13	07	100	
20 12	Trent Jcn	15	16	56*/67	
22 70	Attenborough	18	52	23 pws	
24 16	Beeston	20	37	59/74	
26 20	Lenton South Jcn	22	24	71*	
27 34	Nottingham=22¾	24	50	—	

On the Settle & Carlisle line in September 1970, D34 on the 07.40 Sheffield–Glasgow, with nine coaches, 314/385 tons, put in some remarkable edbhp outputs. So many examples of performances in excess of the class 45 rated outputs have been recorded as to make one wonder just what was going on. In spite of an inauspicious start, due to late running weekend engineering possession, time recovery began at once with a fast start out of Keighley, but it was from Settle that D34's performance became extraordinary. The 1 in 100 climb from Settle Junction to Blea Moor tunnel is broken by slight easings at each station and various other points, but is continuous for the first three miles, on which 56mph was attained. From this point the line climbs out of the wooded cuttings of the Ribble Valley onto the open moorland and starts to wind in great curves from one mountainside to another and over the great viaducts so prolific on this route. Speed rose on the sheltered sections but was pulled down on exposed sections by side winds. The underlying acceleration was maintained: 62mph steady at Selside, 63mph steady past Blea Moor and a final 64mph as the train was half-a-mile inside Blea Moor tunnel. This gave an amazing edbhp output of 2288, but the real revelation was the figure of 2465 at 46½mph on the initial climb out of Settle! A 20-minute late departure from Keighley was reduced to three at Carlisle and on time at Glasgow. Such performances cannot be explained away.

The class 46 variant of the 1Co-Co1 Sulzer is not as good as the class 45. The first batch went to the LMR for use on the Midland line and on north-east/south-west expresses; the second batch of locomotives went to the NER at Gateshead, where they often worked into King's Cross, Edinburgh and Aberdeen, although without any great feats, eth-fitted stock having virtually removed them from such work. They work many of the Newcastle–Liverpool services today. When the WR wanted locomotives, class 46s went rather than 45s, and their use in the south-west is now prolific.

An East Coast run with 46034 on the 16.28 Newcastle–Bristol in September 1975 was loaded to 11 coaches, 376/385 tons, but was diverted via Gateshead due to the stock being in reverse formation after Sunday engineering diversions and resulting in a 23½-minute delay. After a sluggish start, and with 1663edbhp up the 1 in 150 at Plawsworth at 75½mph, the run improved, with 90mph at Bradbury, so that the 22 miles

4 chains to Darlington were run in 21min 9sec, inclusive of the Durham stop. The Darlington–York section appears in Log 4.

Log 4

Train: 16.28 Newcastle–Bristol
Locomotive: 46 034
Nine coaches (Darlington–York section only)

M. Ch.	Location	Min. Sec.	Speed	Edbhp/ mph
0 00	Darlington	0 00	—	
2 48	Croft Spa	3 50	66	2034/71
5 15	Eryholme Jcn	6 01	74	
10 28	Danby Wiske	9 47	87	
14 12	Northallerton	12 26	87	
17 46	Otterington	14 45	91/89	
21 72	Thirsk	17 38	90	
26 05	Sessay	20 24	91	
30 62	Raskelf	23 29	92	
34 30	Tollerton	25 54	90/89	
38 46	Beningborough	28 42	91	
42 38	Skelton Jcn	31 27	59	
44 08	York	34 45	—	

The slight rise out of Darlington gave 2034 edbhp, while leaving York on the next leg of the journey, 2080 edbhp was recorded at 55½mph at Chaloners Whin Junction. South of Sheffield the real test was the 1 in 100 between Sheffield and the south end of Bradway tunnel. This continuous climb, on which 46 034 attained 50mph, gave an edbhp of 2050 at 44½mph. This was not exceptional, but was up to class 45 standard, so very good for a class 46.

The class 47 could be called 'the great might-have-beens'. Some of their early work was certainly impressive, though no more than that of the Peaks which had gone before; but at the time of writing the class 47s have been derated for so long, and with no prospect of their restoration in the foreseeable future, that it is necessary to consider their performances in derated state as the representative ones.

Log 5 features the doyen of the class, D1500, substituting for the booked Deltic on a 'high-speed' limited-load working, unusually made up to nine vehicles instead of eight. The driver kept speed scrupulously to within three points of the limit throughout the run, but otherwise ran as hard as possible, and so did better than average to lose only four minutes on a tight booking. The characteristic of the derated class 47, as compared with its previous performance, is that the strength of the locomotive in the middle speed range seems virtually unaffected, whereas the performance above the electrical unloading point of 80mph tails away dramatically. This gives them a very pronounced speed curve and handicaps them when rapid acceleration into the top ranges of speed is required. Fortunately the East

Coast main line in the up direction makes few demands of this kind, so that the locomotive was able to attain and hold 96–98mph for long distances where the gradients permitted. Nevertheless, the edbhp output figures tell their own story: 1918 at 76mph leaving Darlington, but on the main climbs at 1 in 200, 1496 at 81½mph at Stoke, 1508 at 83½mph at Abbots Ripton and 1542 at 80½mph at Stevenage. This run, fast though it was, involved edbhp mostly 10 per cent inferior to those of an average class 45/1 with the same train and electric train heating load. The first batch of class 47s has remained on East Coast express work, partly because of occasional lapses in Deltic availability and partly because there was nothing to replace them, but the subsequent production series have spread to almost every corner of Britain.

Log 5

Train: 17.00 Newcastle–King's Cross
Locomotive: D1500
Nine coaches; 309/325 tons; Mk II stock

M. Ch.	Location	Min. Sec.	Speed	Edbhp/ mph
0 00	Newcastle	0 00	—	
0 54	King Edward VII Bridge Jcn	3 38	27 (sigs)	
2 49	Low Fell	5 55	68	
5 39	Birtley	8 13	79/77	
8 24	Chester-le-Street	10 18	82/84	
10 63	Kimblesworth	12 07	80/83	
13 70	Durham	14 40	44	
14 66	Relly Mill Jcn	15 57	48/74	
18 02	Croxdale	18 41	68/83	
23 02	Ferryhill	22 42	80	
26 02	Bradbury	24 51	89/92	
30 36	Aycliffe	27 54	54/82	
35 74	Darlington = 33	34 04	—	
2 48	Croft Spa	4 05	71	1918/76
5 15	Eryholme Jcn	6 08	79	
10 28	Danby Wiske	9 37	95	
14 12	Northallerton	12 00	94	
17 46	Otterington	14 09	98	
21 72	Thirsk	16 48	97/96	
26 05	Sessay	19 20	98	
30 62	Raskelf	22 12	98	
34 30	Tollerton	24 38	96	
38 46	Beningborough	27 04	97	
42 38	Skelton Jcn	29 46	58	
44 08	York	32 28	25	
46 04	Challoner's Whin Jcn	35 16	59	
51 11	Escrick	39 20	86/92	
57 75	Selby	44 56	36	
62 40	Templehirst	49 06	80	
66 25	Balne	51 48	91/94	
71 77	Shaftholme Jcn	56 28	90	
76 25	Doncaster	60 56	0 (sigs)	
79 06	Black Carr Jcn	64 45	70/77	
82 60	Pipers Wood	67 39	76/83	
84 43	Bawtry	68 59	77	
88 23	Ranskill	71 46	85/88	
93 50	Retford	75 30	80/83	
98 43	Markham	79 15	76	
104 64	Crow Park	83 26	97	

M.	Ch.	Location	Min.	Sec.	Speed	Edbhpl mph
112	11	Newark	88	17	80	
116	70	Claypole	91	38	88	
122	48	Barkstone South Jcn	95	36	83/81	
126	63	Grantham	98	41	87	1496/81½
132	13	Stoke Box	102	36	77	
135	13	Corby Glen	104	38	95	
140	04	Little Bytham	107	39	98/96	
143	47	Essendine	109	48	97/98	
147	35	Tallington	112	11	97/98	
152	61	Werrington Jcn	115	41	75/77	
155	71	Peterborough	119	16	21	
157	22	Fletton Jcn	122	52	51/83	
162	68	Holme	126	00	80/87	1508/83½
168	62	Abbots Ripton	130	14	78	
173	41	Huntingdon	133	28	97/89	
180	42	St Neots	138	02	90/93/ 89	
184	58	Tempsford	140	55	96/90	
188	10	Sandy	142	56	91/92	
191	07	Biggleswade	144	51	91/87	
195	30	Arlesey	147	35	92	
200	27	Hitchin	151	06	83	1542/80½
204	54	Stevenage	153	36	78	
208	60	Woolmer Green	157	14	86/91	
211	75	Welwyn Garden City	159	22	87/89	
214	47	Hatfield	161	09	80/84	
219	40	Potters Bar	164	48	20 pws	
223	07	New Barnet	170	53	73/91	
227	23	Wood Green	174	01	72	
229	60	Finsbury Park	176	19	60 (sigs)	
232	20	King's Cross=175	182	02	—	

On time at Newcastle and Darlington; four minutes late into King's Cross.

The run in Log 6 is an example of their work with a heavier train on the gradients of the West Coast route, once again as a result of the unavailability of the booked locomotive, this time a class 50. This particular train was at this time scheduled to be double-headed by class 50s in multiple, but was also allowed extra time to cope with engineering work in connection with electrification. The work was at a low level on this weekend, so the single class 47 was able to get away with minimal loss of time. At the more moderate speeds involved climbing to Beattock, the edbhp output was the best of the run, 1850 at 69mph, and compared favourably with the uphill work of the East Coast locomotive. Once again, however, the performance deteriorated as the run went on, and the restart from a signal stop at Nethercleugh gave only 1739 edbhp at 48½mph. The climb from Carlisle to Shap was a little better, with 1861 edbhp at 47½mph on the initial 1 in 131 to Wreay, but fell away again to 1704 edbhp at 56½mph on the long 1 in 125 from Penrith. Downhill work was mostly governed by the gradients, the maximum of 101mph down the 1 in 75 of Shap being made without power at all, but the undulating finish from Weaver Junction to Crewe, averaging a slight rise, found out that the locomotive could not get back above the middle 80s. Edbhp output on this section was approximately 1127 at 84mph, this being only 42 per cent of the nominal bhp at a speed where 65 per cent could reasonably have been expected. In this case no allowance for eth is appropriate as the locomotive was one of the steam-heat only batch.

Log 6

Train: 13.55 Glasgow–Euston
Locomotive: D1858
Twelve coaches; 394/425 tons; steam heat; Mk II stock

M.	Ch.	Location	Min.	Sec.	Speed	Edbhp/ mph
0	00	Glasgow Central	0	00	—	
3	09	Rutherglen	7	43	42/14 pws	
6	44	Newton	14	21	58	
8	32	Uddingston	16	04	72	
12	65	Motherwell	20	25	51	
14	74	Shieldmuir Jcn	22	20	54	
18	14	Law Jcn	26	37	49/54	
20	23	Carluke	29	04	52/51	
23	62	Craigenhill	33	08	56	
26	11	Lanark Jcn	35	27	80	
28	50	Carstairs	37	21	61/63 pws	
32	16	Leggatfoot	40	45	62	
33	59	Thankerton	42	05	72/65	
35	44	Symington	43	34	67	
39	01	Lamington	46	27	84/85	
44	31	Abington	50	31	77/68	
49	50	Elvanfoot	54	45	73/75	1850/69
52	44	Beattock Summit	57	18	63	
56	68	Greskine	60	30	90/82	
62	40	Beattock	64	27	87/89	
67	58	Wamphray	68	05	84/80	
70	37	Dinwoodie	70	03	88/0 (sigs)	1739/48½
76	32	Lockerbie	78	52	63/68	
80	19	Milepost 22	82	18	67/89	
85	40	Kirtlebridge	86	08	83/85/ 82	
89	19	Kirkpatrick	88	52	88/85	
93	41	Gretna Jcn	91	46	88	
100	13	Kingmoor Box	96	24	83	
102	19	Carlisle=88	98	52	—	
2	08	Milepost 67	4	07	45	1861/47½
4	73	Wreay	7	32	53	
7	29	Southwaite	10	04	60	
10	53	Calthwaite	13	22	63	
13	06	Plumpton	15	38	69/72	
15	48	Milepost 53½	17	46	68/72	
17	68	Penrith	19	51	56/66	
21	11	Eden Valley Jcn	23	03	65	1704/56½
25	08	Milepost 44	27	08	54	
27	54	Harrisons Sidings	29	58	54	
29	30	Shap	31	52	59/56	
31	39	Shap Summit	34	04	61	
36	78	Tebay	37	48	101	
42	78	Grayrigg	42	16	72/88	
46	47	Hay Fell	44	55	79	
50	01	Oxenholme	47	24	85/84	
55	45	Milnthorpe	51	18	89	
59	48	Milepost 9½	54	13	81/93	
62	68	Carnforth	56	25	86/81	
66	00	Hest Bank	58	41	85	
69	08	Lancaster	61	11	59	
70	13	Lancaster Old Jcn	62	21	54	

M.	Ch.	Location	Min.	Sec.	Speed	Edbhpl mph
72	07	Oubeck	64	16	67	
74	67	Bay Horse	66	32	79/17 pws	
77	31	Scorton	71	03	43	
80	49	Garstang	74	18	71	
82	49	Brock	75	54	78	
85	27	Barton	77	57	81/84	
90	07	Preston=79½	83	18	—	
1	48	Farington Curve Jcn	3	07	52/51	
4	02	Leyland	5	47	62/61	
6	60	Balshaw Lane	8	19	71/73	
10	37	Coppull Hall	11	36	66	
12	77	Boars Head Jcn	13	29	83/51 (sigs)	
15	09	Wigan	15	50	57/78	
17	60	Bamfurlong	18	08	76/72	
21	01	Golborne Jcn	20	44	78	
23	34	Winwick Jcn	21	41	68	
26	70	Warrington	24	36	77/71	
29	66	Moore	26	54	83/77	
34	41	Weaver Jcn	30	27	82	
39	18	Hartford	33	25	84/87	
43	42	Winsford	36	56	85/83	
47	65	Coppenhall Jcn	40	01	84	1127/84
50	77	Crewe=43¾	44	20	—	

Left Glasgow on time; 8½ minutes late at Carlisle;
2½ minutes late at Preston; 4½ minutes late at Crewe.
Running on extended schedule due to electrification work.

The main development has been the fitting of a similar electronic control system to that used in the class 50s to many locomotives of what is now class 47/4, the eth-fitted batch, and hence the ones most frequently used on top-link passenger services. This system employs solid-state devices, and thus has much greater economy in power absorption compared with conventional resistance-controlled locomotives. The system has not been infallible, but when working correctly it has given the locomotives a much-needed 5 per cent or so extra at the drawbar. An example of this latest new level of performance is the run in Log 7, where yet another substitution had been made. This time it was a limited-load locomotive-hauled set replacing an HST, due to late delivery of the latter when their interim timings were first introduced in October 1976. Several such workings were run for a while, mostly with 100mph class 50s between Paddington and Bristol. South Wales had first choice of the HST units, but a few class 47s had to go out, since Landore and Cardiff men had not been trained on the class 50s. This would not have been all that bad, since the interim timings were a good deal slower than the permanent timings from May 1977, but unfortunately this particular working converged at Wootton Bassett with an HST from Bristol; the latter was naturally given priority, and the arrival was 19 minutes late in consequence. In between, however, the superior performance was

immediately apparent. The climb out of the Severn Tunnel at 1 in 100 was worth 1861 edbhp at 62mph, while that of the 1 in 300 to Badminton gave 1813 edbhp at 75mph. There was no difficulty in working up to the permitted 95mph or so down the gentle descent from Swindon to Paddington with such a light load; nevertheless, the edbhp output tailed off sharply once again as the higher ranges of speed were reached, to 1637 at 85mph near Didcot, 1493 at 91mph leaving Reading and 1445 at 92mph after Swindon. Train heating in this case accounted for a further 235hp.

Log 7
Train: 11.00 Swansea–Paddington
Locomotive: 47 502
Eight coaches; 270/285 tons; eth 36; Mk II stock

M.	Ch.	Location	Min.	Sec.	Speed	Edbhp/ mph
0	00	Cardiff	0	00	—	
2	40	Rumney Bridge Jcn	4	04	66/77	
6	42	Marshfield	7	18	73/76	
10	21	Ebbw Jcn	10	23	61	
11	59	Newport	13	08	—	
1	47	East Usk Box	2	55	62/75	
5	49	Bishton Crossing	6	17	73/75	
9	70	Severn Tunnel Jcn	9	50	70/58 pws	
15	27	Severn Tunnel East	15	08	61 att.	1861/62
16	65	Pilning	16	35	62/68	
20	31	Patchway	22	13	18 pws/ 62	
21	55	Bristol Parkway=20	23	51	—	
1	74	Winterbourne	3	01	62 (sigs)	
4	49	Westerleigh Jcn	5	27	70	1813/75
7	16	Chipping Sodbury	7	31	78	
11	61	Badminton	10	53	83	
17	40	Hullavington	14	37	96/97	
22	00	Little Somerford	17	35	94/95	
28	71	Wootton Bassett	27	02	0 (sigs)	
34	38	Swindon	32	17	86	
36	59	Stratton Park	33	48	91/96	1445/92
40	19	Shrivenham	36	05	89	
45	16	Uffington	39	13	97	
47	75	Challow	40	56	94/93	
51	27	Wantage Road	43	05	95/97	
55	20	Steventon	45	32	96/63 (sigs)	
58	50	Didcot	48	25	73	1637/85
63	24	Cholsey	51	43	91	
67	01	Goring	54	04	96/97	
70	18	Pangbourne	56	04	94/0 (sigs)	
75	63	Reading=55	57	58	—	
2	01	Sonning	3	17	62	
4	77	Twyford	5	39	84	1493/91
7	75	Shottesbrook	7	40	92	
11	59	Maidenhead	10	03	96/94	
15	02	Burnham	12	08	95/93	
17	43	Slough	13	45	94/95	
19	60	Langley	15	11	93/92	
22	61	West Drayton	17	06	93/94	
25	06	Hayes	18	33	93	
26	72	Southall	19	47	88	

M. Ch.	Location	Min. Sec. Speed	Edbhpl mph
30 20	Ealing Broadway	22 04 90	
33 15	Old Oak Common Box	24 06 81	
35 73	Paddington	27 59 —	

Left Cardiff 3½ minutes late; 4½ minutes late at Newport;
3½ minutes late at Parkway; 21 minutes late at Reading;
19 minutes late into Paddington.
Temporary substitute for HST set, running on HST schedule.

The class 48 remains something of a mystery, in that the smaller, lighter and faster engine with which the locomotives were fitted was said to be a success mechanically, yet after several years' service was removed in favour of the standard power unit. The locomotives themselves spent most of their time on heavy freight work over the generally level route between Tinsley and Whitemoor, but towards the end of their career were transferred to express work between Liverpool Street and Norwich. Log 8 is a run made at the time with the standard load and schedule. The route is a difficult one on which to make power assessments, as the gradients are anything but constant.

Log 8
Train: 17.40 Norwich–Liverpool Street
Locomotive: D1705
Ten coaches; 348/375 tons

M. Ch.	Location	Min. Sec. Speed	Edbhp/ mph
0 00	Norwich	0 00 —	
2 28	Trowse Upper Jcn	5 26 39/68	
5 40	Swainsthorpe	8 45 65	
8 41	Flordon	11 15 78/80	
11 10	Forncett	13 13 77/82	
14 51	Tivetshall	15 49 80/78	
17 55	Burston	18 08 81/55 pws	
20 17	Diss	20 26 65/76	
23 67	Mellis	23 24 70/74	
28 52	Finningham	27 21 71/77	
32 23	Haughley	30 22 65	
34 48	Stowmarket	32 17 74/78	
38 09	Needham	35 00 77/80	
41 54	Claydon	37 43 74/78	
43 79	Bramford	39 46 41/55 (sigs)	
46 38	Ipswich=42½	44 01 —	
3 59	Milepost 65	5 12 57/79	
9 44	Manningtree	9 58 65	
11 01	Dedham Box	11 21 65	1984/65
12 59	Ardleigh	13 00 58 pws	
14 59	Parsons Heath Box	14 42 75/84	
17 11	Colchester=16¾	17 21 —	
2 48	Stanway	3 41 56	
5 00	Marks Tey	5 53 75	
9 27	Kelvedon	9 07 92/88	
13 00	Witham	11 36 89/84	1655/86
15 59	Hatfield Peverel	13 30 88/90	
19 37	New Hall	15 48 88	
21 70	Chelmsford	18 01 53	
25 48	Milepost 26	21 21 75	
28 00	Ingatestone	23 18 71/5 (sigs)	

M. Ch.	Location	Min. Sec. Speed	mph
31 32	Shenfield	27 59 39	
33 32	Brentwood	30 26 60/69	
38 06	Gidea Park	34 38 57 (sigs)	
39 17	Romford	35 43 67	
44 20	Ilford	40 31 57/59	
47 49	Stratford	44 17 44/0 (sigs)	
51 48	Liverpool Street=47½	54 25 —	

Left Norwich on time; 2½ minutes late at Ipswich; on time at Colchester and into London.

Kestrel was another might-have-been, but never really achieved anything like its potential. For its brief trial on the East Coast main line it worked mostly on the limited-load 07.55 King's Cross–Newcastle and 16.45 return, of which the run in Log 9 is an example. Naturally the locomotive had no difficulty in attaining 100mph and more on the level track of this main line, so interest is confined in the main to its acceleration on the 1 in 200 ruling grades. For assessment purposes the run was conveniently interrupted at the bottom of the climbs to both Potters Bar and Stoke. The recovery from the former involved an edbhp output of 2582 at 75mph, while on the latter the figure was 2679 at 71mph. The final section of Stoke bank steepens to 1 in 178, and on this the effort had fallen to 2289 edbhp at 90mph. The effort was therefore quite consistent across a wide range of speeds and gradients, as was confirmed by a further figure of 2710 edbhp at 68mph accelerating out of York on the level; nevertheless, it was fairly mediocre for a locomotive supposedly capable of 4000hp at some point in the proceedings. It was, in short, insufficiently superior to a Deltic to justify further investment.

Log 9
Train: 07.55 King's Cross–Newcastle
Locomotive: HS4000 *Kestrel*
Eight coaches; 276/290 tons; Mk II stock

M. Ch.	Location	Min. Sec. Speed	Edbhp/ mph
0 00	King's Cross	0 00 —	
2 40	Finsbury Park	4 55 59/0 (sigs)	
9 13	New Barnet	21 01 68	2582/75
12 60	Potters Bar	23 50 82/78	
17 53	Hatfield	27 35 85/92	
20 25	Welwyn Garden City	29 20 86/95	
23 40	Woolmer Green	31 27 88/94	
28 45	Stevenage	34 46 91/95	
31 73	Hitchin	36 58 89/104	
36 70	Arlesey	40 08 98/105	
41 13	Biggleswade	42 35 104/97	
44 10	Sandy	44 20 102/105	
47 42	Tempsford	46 19 99/102	
51 58	St Neots	49 44 54/87 (sigs)	
55 75	Offord	52 56 73	
58 59	Huntingdon	55 10 89	

62 00	Milepost 62	57 14	94	
69 32	Holme	62 11	68/83	
76 29	Peterborough	68 44	18	
79 39	Werrington Jcn	72 43	63/61	
84 65	Tallington	76 41	98/103	
88 53	Essendine	79 01	101/104	
92 16	Little Bytham	83 01	14	
			(sigs)	
93 00	Milepost 93	83 54	59	2679/71
96 00	Milepost 96	86 26	80	
97 07	Corby Glen	87 14	89	2289/90
100 07	Stoke Box	89 13	91/94	
105 37	Grantham	92 51	70	
109 52	Barkston South Jcn	95 52	102/100	
115 30	Claypole	99 13	106	
120 09	Newark	102 14	78/61	
126 28	Carlton-on-Trent	107 15	84/88	
133 57	Markham	112 37	78/87	
138 50	Retford	116 07	76	
143 77	Ranskill	120 05	84/20	
			pws	
149 40	Pipers Wood	126 52	68/73	
153 14	Black Carr Jcn	130 16	58/62	
155 75	Doncaster	133 13	58	
160 23	Shaftholme Jcn	137 22	69	
163 00	Moss	139 18	83	
167 15	Heck	142 07	95	
174 25	Selby	147 18	38	
178 38	Riccall	151 17	87/93	
186 15	Challoner's Whin Jcn	156 56	49/62	
188 12	York	159 43	22	
189 62	Skelton Jcn	162 29	68	2710/68
193 54	Beningborough	165 21	95/104	
197 70	Tollerton	167 51	102/105	
201 38	Raskelf	170 00	101	
206 15	Sessay	172 45	105/106	
210 28	Thirsk	175 10	102/106	
214 54	Otterington	177 42	103/105	
218 08	Northallerton	179 44	100	
221 72	Danby Wiske	181 56	106/107	
227 05	Eryholme Jcn	185 04	80	
232 20	Darlington=173½	191 12	—	
5 38	Aycliffe	6 54	70/56	
9 72	Bradbury	10 23	81/31	
			(sigs)	
12 72	Ferryhill	13 58	62/84	
17 72	Croxdale	18 02	74/78	
22 04	Durham	23 05	19 pws	
23 20	Newton Hall Jcn	25 25	61/56	
25 74	Plawsworth	27 42	81/86	
30 50	Birtley	34 47	14/76	
			(sigs)	
35 35	King Edward VII			
	Bridge Jcn	40 06	21	
36 09	Newcastle=36½	43 25	—	

Left King's Cross on time; 2½ minutes late at Darlington;
6½ minutes late into Newcastle.

Performance results from the trials on the WR with *Lion* have not been made available for examination. The reason for this could be its failings and the reticence to re-awaken interest in the 15-year-old controversy surrounding its withdrawal and subsequent scrapping. Fortunately,

Rodney Weaver was able to sample its prowess during its brief sojourn on the Wolverhampton–Paddington services in 1962. With the 07.30 ex-Wolverhampton, *Lion* took the 11-coach 385/400-ton load on the 102-minute schedule with complete ease, in spite of successive signal checks, two signal stops and permanent way restrictions. A maximum of 105mph was reached, and many sections were covered with averages around 80 and 90mph. Edbhp outputs were 1548 at 53½mph and 2227 at 85½mph, and as its published performance curve indicates, *Lion* was able to use full power over the 17½–86mph range, against 11–80mph for the original 2750bhp class 47, making *Lion* more suitable for passenger work than freight work. *Lion* remains perhaps the biggest mystery of British diesel traction in post-war times.

TABLE 21
YEARS OF WITHDRAWAL FOR THE BRITISH RAIL SULZER LOCOMOTIVES, INCLUDING ACCIDENT VICTIMS; LIST EXCLUDES REINSTATEMENTS TO STOCK AFTER FIRST WITHDRAWAL, GIVING FINAL WITHDRAWAL YEAR ONLY
(Original numbering used)

Year	Nos of withdrawn locomotives	Total withdrawn
1964	D6502	1
1965	D1734	1
1966	D1671, D5383	2
1967	D5051	1
1968	D6576	1
1969	D1908, D5005/43/93, D5122/38/9	7
1970	D5088	1
1971	D1562, D5131, D5278	3
1972	D5028/67/8, D5114/49, D5328, D7605	7
1973		0
1974		0
1975	D5001–4/6–8/10–21/4/6/9/31/3/42/5/8/50/5/6/8–62/71/2/4/6/92/5/6/8, D5105/36/48/65/95, D5316/98, D6558	51
1976	D5000/9/22/5/7/30/2/4/7–41/4/6/9/52–4/64–6/9/70/5/7–80/3–6/9 90/4/7/9, D5100–4/6–13/5–21/3–30/2/4/5/7/40–7/50/3/4/66–8/70/2/4/80, D5352/9, D7524	92
1977	D115/42, D5036/91, D5162/4/75/9/81, D5246, D5300/9/61	13

Notes   D5032 on loan from T. & J. Thompson Stockton on Tees to North Yorkshire Moors Railway
D5054/61 now TDB968008/7 and allocated to the WR for carriage preheating duties.
D5142 now TDB968009 and allocated to BR Research Centre Derby for working test trains.

INDEX